D1287647

CLUES

I CLU ES 0410943 F

Q 632
Jacobson, Jay S. ed.
   Recognition of air pollution
injury to vegetation: a pictorial
atlas

Date Due

Q 632
Jacobson, Jay S. ed.
   Recognition of air pollution
injury to vegetation: a pictorial atlas

CUMBERLAND COUNTY LIBRARY
BRIDGETON, N.J.   08302

PRINTED IN U.S.A.

Recognition of Air Pollution Injury to Vegetation: A Pictorial Atlas

Edited by: Jay S. Jacobson
A. Clyde Hill

Prepared under the auspices of
Air Pollution Control Association
and
National Air Pollution Control Administration

AIR POLLUTION CONTROL ASSOCIATION
Pittsburgh, Pennsylvania
1970

Lithographed by Herbick & Held Printing Co., Pittsburgh, Pa.
© Copyright 1970 by the Air Pollution Control Association.

PREFACE

This Atlas, published as Informative Report No. 1 of the TR-7 Agricultural Committee, Air Pollution Control Association, resulted from a three-year project culminating in the Symposium on "Recognition of Air Pollution Injury to Vegetation" presented at the Association's annual meeting in New York City, June 22-26, 1969. The idea for the Symposium was initiated by the Air Pollution Research Grants Advisory Committee of the U. S. Public Health Service in 1966. The TR-7 Agricultural organized and sponsored the Symposium, which was chaired by the editors of this Atlas. Previously, a technical seminar, sponsored by the National Air Pollution Control Administration was held in December 1968. A panel of twenty-two experts reviewed and evaluated photographs of vegetation injury for inclusion in this Atlas.

This publication was made possible by the dedicated support and effort of many individuals and organizations. The National Air Pollution Control Administration generously provided financial assistance in the project, and several individuals from that organization gave technical assistance which contributed greatly to the final publication. These include: Mr. Owen Nichols, former Head of the Office of Technical Information and Publications; Mr. Robert Kolbinsky, Chief of the Technical Publications Branch; and Dr. Walter Heck, Chief, Agriculture Branch and Plant Physiologist, U. S. Department of Agriculture.

The Air Pollution Control Association supported this effort from inception to publication. The assistance of Mr. Lloyd G. Transtrum, Chairman of the TR-7 Agricultural Committee was indispensable in this regard. The advice and assistance of Mr. Harold M. Englund, Editor of the *Journal of the Air Pollution Control Association* was extremely valuable and is gratefully acknowledged. North Carolina State University provided the services of Mrs. Margaret Goode, who prepared the manuscript for publication, under cooperative agreement No. 12-14-100-10,368(34) with the U.S. Department of Agriculture.

Thanks are also due to Mr. John Dunning, research biologist, National Air Pollution Control Administration, who verified and indexed the botanical plant names. Other individuals, too numerous to mention, supported and made contributions to this Atlas. The editors hope that this publication will prove to be a source of satisfaction to all.

LIST OF AUTHORS

Barrett, Thomas W.
  Arizona State University, Tempe, Arizona

Benedict, Harris M.
  Stanford Research Institute, Palo Alto, California

Daines, Robert H.
  Rutgers University, New Brunswick, New Jersey

Heck, Walter W.
  U. S. Department of Agriculture and National Air Pollution Control Administration, Raleigh, North Carolina

Heggestad, Howard E.
  U. S. Department of Agriculture, Beltsville, Maryland

Hill, A. Clyde
  University of Utah, Salt Lake City, Utah

Hindawi, Ibrahim J.
  National Air Pollution Control Administration, Cincinnati, Ohio

Jacobson, Jay S.
  Boyce Thompson Institute for Plant Research, Yonkers, New York

Linzon, Samuel N.
  Ontario Department of Energy and Resources Management, Toronto

MacLean, David C.
  Boyce Thompson Institute for Plant Research, Yonkers, New York

McCune, Delbert C.
  Boyce Thompson Institute for Plant Research, Yonkers, New York

Pack, Merrill R.
  Washington State University, Pullman, Washington

Taylor, O. Clifton
  University of California, Riverside, California

Treshow, Michael
  University of Utah, Salt Lake City, Utah

Weinstein, Leonard H.
  Boyce Thompson Institute for Plant Research, Yonkers, New York

TABLE OF CONTENTS

LIST OF FIGURES

LIST OF TABLES

Introduction

Jay S. Jacobson
Boyce Thompson Institute for Plant Research, Yonkers, New York
and
A. Clyde Hill
University of Utah, Salt Lake City, Utah

Injury to vegetation induced by exposure to air pollutants has become a major factor in evaluating the impact of mans' activities on the environment. Such an evaluation is essential before we can develop effective solutions to environmental problems because history indicates that adequate control of emissions has usually followed the identification of a specific air pollution problem. Recognition of pollutant-induced effects and identification of the specific causal agent or agents is a complex task requiring integration of knowledge from several diverse fields. Available knowledge concerning the recognition of air pollution injury to plants has been compiled and forms the basic contribution of this Atlas.

Observations of injury on sensitive plant species have provided a means of monitoring pollutant emissions from a source, and, because air sampling data has seldom been available, observations of plant injury have also been a valuable tool for determining the geographical distribution of a pollutant over a large area. For example, the occurrence and distribution of peroxyacetyl nitrate-induced symptoms in the United States have been established based on observations of vegetation injury although few analyses of the concentration of peroxyacetyl nitrate in ambient air have been available. Consequently it has become increasingly important to accurately identify air pollution effects on vegetation and to distinguish these effects from injury resulting from other environmental factors.

When plants are injured by an air pollutant, symptoms characteristic of the specific pollutant usually develop. Since the pollutant itself normally undergoes chemical change soon after it contacts plant tissue, symptoms are often the only remaining evidence of pollutant assault. Thus, symptoms provide the major basis for diagnosis. In this Atlas, the characteristic symptoms of the major phytotoxic pollutants are described in Chapters B through F and are illustrated with colored photographs. All of the major phytotoxic air pollutants and the methods used to recognize and identify the resulting injury to plants are described. Important diagnostic tools such as relative susceptibility of different species, pollutant concentrations required to cause injury, and where appropriate, leaf analysis are discussed. The last chapter outlines a reasoned approach to the recognition of injury by discussing the methods used for obtaining information pertinent to the problem; it discusses the value of field surveys, air monitoring, chemical analyses, and indicator plants in leading to accurate diagnosis.

The color photographs of air pollutant-induced symptoms on agronomic, horticultural, and forest plants were obtained as a result of either experimental laboratory or greenhouse fumigations or from field exposures. Certain pollutant-induced symptoms may be similar to those caused by diseases or other debilitating factors, but an experienced observer can, after making careful observations, usually determine the cause of injury. These mimicking symptoms are also portrayed for most pollutants and figures illustrating them are included in several chapters. Factors which affect sensitivity, including the interaction between environmental and/or biological influences and pollution-induced effects are discussed. The subtle effects of pollutants, such as effects on growth, premature senescence, abnormalities in flowering or fruiting, and genetic or biochemical changes are active areas of research and are not generally used as diagnostic aids.

The experience and knowledge of the fourteen authors qualify them to describe the information and approaches used to recognize air pollution injury to vegetation. All chapters have been reviewed to achieve a reasonable degree of uniformity but final decisions on content were the responsibility of the chapter authors. It is hoped that the Atlas will assist technical personnel to recognize the visible effects of pollutants on vegetation and aid in the assessment of these effects on our total environment.

Ozone

A. Clyde Hill
University of Utah, Salt Lake City, Utah
Howard E. Heggestad
United States Department of Agriculture, Beltsville, Maryland
and
Samuel N. Linzon
Ontario Department of Energy and Resources Management, Toronto

Introduction

Vegetation injury induced by photochemical smog was first reported in 1944 in the Los Angeles basin.[1] In 1958 Richards *et al.*[2] showed that ozone was a phytotoxic constituent of the smog complex when they identified injury by ozone to grape foliage in California. The next year, Heggestad and Middleton[3] reported that ozone was the cause of extensive injury to tobacco in the eastern United States. Following this, various investigators showed that ozone was responsible for injury to many agronomic crops, horticultural crops, deciduous trees, etc.[4-8] Also investigation of unexplained needle injuries to white pine in the east and to ponderosa pine in the west have shown that many of the needle disorders are attributable to atmospheric oxidants, of which ozone makes up the greatest part.[9-13] These diseases are described in this paper as ozone injury of eastern white pine[14], chlorotic dwarf of eastern white pine[11], and chlorotic decline of ponderosa pine.[13, 15]

Ozone probably causes more injury to vegetation than any other air pollutant in the United States. Many species and varieties of plants are sensitive to ozone and elevated concentrations frequently occur over large areas near the more densely populated regions. Concentrations high enough to injure sensitive species have been observed more than 70 miles from large metropolitan sources such as Philadelphia, New York and Los Angeles. Injury to leaves, where they themselves are the marketable products (*e.g.,* tobacco and spinach), can result in reduced quality or loss of the crop. Also reduction in growth and yield of many species may result from ozone injury.

Although ozone concentrations as high as 4 pphm may occur in remote desert regions due to transport from the upper atmosphere[16], concentrations high enough to injure plants apparently result from photochemical reactions in the lower atmosphere. Photolysis of nitrogen dioxide and the concomitant removal of the nitric oxide produced by reaction with hydrocarbon free radicals results in the build-up of ozone. The precursors (oxides of nitrogen and hydrocarbons) are emitted into the atmosphere in densely populated regions from automobiles, industrial combustion, oil refineries, and various more limited sources.

Relative Susceptibility

Considerable varietal and species differences in ozone sensitivity have been observed, but data are inadequate to permit a detailed listing of the relative sensitivity of different species and varieties. Some of the species which have been observed to be injured in the field or which have appeared sensitive in fumigations are listed in Table B-I.

In fumigation experiments, ozone concentrations between 5 and 12 pphm for 2-4 hrs are usually required to injure the most sensitive species. For example, certain varieties of tobacco have been injured by ozone concentrations as low as 5 pphm for 4 hrs. Eastern white pine has been injured by 7 pphm for 4 hrs,[14] and sensitive varieties of alfalfa, spinach, clover, oats, radish, sweet corn, and bean have been injured by 10-12 pphm for 2 hrs.[16] In the presence of sulfur dioxide, ozone concentrations as low as 3 pphm have produced typical injury to a sensitive variety of tobacco apparently because of synergistic effects.[17] Species such as euonymus (*Euonymus,* sp.), Pfitzer juniper, (*Juniperus Chinensis* var. *Pfitzeriana,* Spaeth), and yew (*Taxus,* sp.) appear to be quite resistant to ozone since they failed to develop injury during exposure to concentrations as high as 100 pphm.[16]

Response of plants to ozone is dependent on various environmental factors.[18,19] Stomatal closure caused by moisture stress or other factors can protect even the sensitive species from injury.[16,20] There is some evidence that ozone itself may induce stomatal closure, thus reducing the amount of ozone entering the leaf and contributing to the resistance to ozone injury of certain varieties.[21] The stage of plant growth, nutrition, light, relative humidity, temperature, and various other factors may determine the response to a given ozone dosage. For this reason the same ozone concentration may cause little or no injury at one time or place, and extensive injury at another time or in a different location. There is some evidence that growth of plants may be suppressed even in the absence of visible evidence of injury since carbon dioxide assimilation may be reduced during ozone exposure even when visible injury is absent.[22,24] Little is known about the relative susceptibility of different species to growth suppression.

B 1

TABLE B-I
Selected plants, certain varieties or clones of which are relatively sensitive to ozone[a,b]

Crops

Alfalfa
Medicago sativa, L.
Barley
Hordeum vulgare, L.
Bean
Phaseolus vulgaris, L.
Clover, red
Trifolium pratense, L.
Corn, sweet
Zea mays, L.
Grass, bent
Agrostis palustris, Huds.
Grass, brome
Bromus inermis, Leyss.

Grass, crab
Digitaria sanguinalis, L.
Grass, orchard
Dactylis glomerata, L.
Muskmelon
Cucumis melo, L.
Oat
Avena sativa, L.
Onion
Allium cepa, L.
Peanut
Arachis hypogaea, L.
Potato
Solanum tuberosum, L.

Radish
Raphanus sativus, L.
Rye
Secale cereale, L.
Spinach
Spinacea oleracea, L.
Tobacco
Nicotiana tabacum, L.
Tomato
Lycopersicon esculentum, Mill.
Wheat
Triticum Aestivum, L.

Trees, Shrubs, and Ornamentals

Alder
Alnus, sp.
Apple, crab
Malus baccata, Borkh.
Aspen, quaking
Populus tremuloides, Michx.
Boxelder
Acer negundo, L.
Bridalwreath
Spiraea prunifolia, Sieb. & Zucc.
Carnation
Dianthus caryophyllus, L.
Catalpa
Catalpa speciosa, Warder

Chrysanthemum
Chrysanthemum, sp.
Grape
Vitis vinifera, L.
Honeylocust
Gleditsia triacanthos, L.
Lilac
Syringa vulgaris, L.
Maple, silver
Acer saccharinum, L.
Oak, gambel
Quercus gambelii
Petunia
Petunia hybrida, Vilm.

Pine, eastern white
Pinus strobus, L.
Pine, ponderosa
Pinus ponderosa, Laws.
Privet
Ligustrum vulgare, L.
Snowberry
Symphoricarpos albus, Blake
Sycamore
Platanus occidentalis, L.
Weeping Willow
Salix babylonica, L.

[a]Generally the crops listed are more sensitive than the trees and shrubs.
[b]Listing of plants came from references 2-9, 13, 16, 30, 32, and 41-47.

Symptomatology

There are several factors that should be considered when attempting to determine if ozone is the cause of plant injury. Knowledge of the concentration of ozone in the atmosphere, the concentration required to injure the more sensitive species, and the species that are most likely to become injured is valuable. These areas were briefly covered in the preceding section. The common ozone lesion types and the location of injury on the leaf or plant form the major basis for diagnosis and these factors will be discussed in this section.

Although it may be of questionable diagnostic value, the possibility of reduced growth should be kept in mind. For example, tobacco, various grasses, beans, potatoes, ornamental plants, and tree species grown in the unfiltered greenhouses at the U. S. Dept. of Agriculture Air Pollution Laboratory in Beltsville, Md., were all significantly smaller than those grown in the air-filtered greenhouses. Ozone appeared to be the pollutant responsible for the leaf injury and reduction in growth of these plants. When ozone injury occurs frequently during the growing season, reduced growth may form a significant part of the injury syndrome.

Lesion Types

For convenience, ozone injury lesions are discussed under four different general types. Usually only one type of injury is present, but two or three different lesion types may be present on a single leaf or on different plants in the same area. (Figure B-1 shows two different injury types resulting from the same fumigation.)

Pigmented lesions. The most common symptom on many deciduous trees and shrubs, and some herbaceous species, is localized thickening and pigmentation of the cell walls resulting in sharply defined, small dot-like lesions.[7] Palisade cells are most prone to ozone injury and on leaves with palisade parenchyma, primary lesions are often limited to small groups of palisade cells and the injury is observable primarily on the upper leaf surface. The lesions may be dark brown, black, purple, or red. Measurement of ozone-induced biosynthesis of certain anthocyanins in dock (*Rumex crispus*, L.) indicates that anthocyanin may be one of the important pigments formed.[25] Occasionally pigments formed in the injured tissue of some species diffuse into surrounding tissue and veins. Epidermal tissue overlying the injured palisade cells usually remains uninjured. Unless the pigment diffuses through the tissue, the injury is evident primarily on the upper leaf surface (Figure B-2). Primary lesions take up all or part of the space between the smallest veins so the size and shape of the lesions are largely determined by these veins (Figures B-3 and B-4). For this reason the lesions are usually angular in shape, often approximating a square with somewhat rounded sides. These symptoms can often be observed best under low magnification and with transmitted rather than reflected light. Use of a hand lens, while holding the leaf up to the sun, will usually show the lesions well. Typical symptoms observed with transmitted light are shown in Figure B-5. The veins are usually not affected except in species where pigments color sections of veins (Figure B-6). Pigment formation can produce an overall coloration of the upper leaf surface when the lesions are dense (Figures B-2 and B-7).

Upper-surface or either-surface bleaching. Small unpigmented necrotic spots or more general upper-surface bleaching is a common type of injury on most herbaceous and many woody species.[7] Palisade cells, and, when the injury is more severe, upper-epidermis cells collapse and become bleached. Upper-surface necrotic areas can become relatively large before an appreciable amount of necrosis extends through to the lower surface. Sometimes small necrotic lesions occur in the center of larger chlorotic spots, but usually chlorosis is absent. As the cells collapse, connection is usually retained to the cells immediately above and below, and the resulting air space gives the tissue a light gray, milk-white, or tan color (Figure B-8). The individual lesions are usually small (Figures B-9 and B-10), but they may become fairly large on certain herbaceous species and frequently result in slightly sunken areas on the upper leaf surface (Figure B-11). Individual lesions tend to be irregular in shape. Injury can develop on either leaf surface on species such as small grains and grasses since they lack palisade tissue. On rare occasions lower-surface injury develops on other species such as tomatoes. Figures B-1 and B-9 through B-19 show typical upper-surface necrotic lesions on herbaceous plants, and Figures B-20 through B-23 show typical lesions on trees.

Bifacial necrosis. When all of the tissue through the leaf is killed, relatively large bifacial necrotic areas develop (Figures B-1, B-10, B-11, B-18, B-19, B-23 through B-27). Necrotic tissue ranges from almost white (Figure B-1) to orange-red, (Figure B-26) depending on the species. The upper and lower surfaces are often drawn together forming a thin, papery lesion. Small veins are usually killed along with other tissue, although the larger veins frequently survive (Figures B-12 and B-24). Upper-surface necrosis and bifacial necrosis often occur on a single leaf (Figures B-10 and B-11), the bifacial necrosis usually being darker in color.

A shiny, oily or waxy appearance of the upper leaf surface develops during exposure to ozone on some species such as spinach. Much of the oily appearance disappears within a few hours after termination of exposure. Permanently injured areas may become dull gray-green during or following fumigation. A water-soaked appearance often develops followed by drying and bleaching which results in typical bifacial necrosis within 1 or 2 days.

Chlorosis. On leaves with palisade parenchyma, primary lesions are usually limited to small groups of palisade cells and the injury is observable primarily on the upper leaf surface. Epidermal tissue overlying injured palisade cells and underlying spongy mesophyll cells usually remain uninjured. The size of primary lesions ranges from a few cells to about 1 mm in diameter; however, the lesions may merge to give a yellow mottled appearance. Many of the injured cells remain alive but when these are examined under the microscope, disrupted chloroplasts and reduced amounts of chlorophyll can be detected.[5] Species such as grasses with undifferentiated mesophyll may develop a fine chlorotic stippling on either surface (Figure B-28). The outer spongy mesophyll cells appear to be the most readily affected in these plants, although chlorosis may extend completely through the leaf. Chlorotic mottling or chlorotic flecks are common symptoms on pine (Figures B-27, B-29 and B-30), but they are less common than the other injury type on most species. Sometimes species such as alfalfa develop large, light green chlorotic areas with many irregular islands of normal green tissue dispersed in them (Figure B-17). Several days after being exposed to a high ozone concentration or after a low-level, long-term exposure, older leaves, which may or may not show necrotic lesions, sometimes turn yellow and become senescent prematurely (Figure B-14). In this case much of the tissue eventually becomes uniformly chlorotic and the leaves may drop prematurely.[7]

Location of Injury

The location of injury with respect to position on the leaf and degree of maturity of leaves is frequently of significant diagnostic value.

Position on leaf. The fact that injury is often limited to the upper leaf surface has been discussed previously. Injury also tends to develop towards the tip of the youngest leaves that are affected and over the whole leaf or towards the base of the oldest leaves that are affected.[7] Markings often consist of a band of injured tissue across the leaf in which only tissue of a certain age is affected. For example, sweet corn leaves usually develop bands of necrosis about 5-13 cm long. Injury is located towards the tip of the youngest injured leaf, towards the center of the next older leaves and towards the base of the oldest injured leaf. Younger and older leaves are free from injury. Often, with plants such as ash (*Fraxinus,* sp.) or walnut (*Juglans,* sp.) with pinnately compound leaves, only leaflets in a certain position along the petiole are affected. When plants are exposed to ozone periodically during growth (the common type of field exposure) much of the tissue on the older leaves may show injury. Typical bands of injury on corn leaves following a single exposure are shown in Figure B-24, and a leaf that has been subjected to several ozone exposures in the field is shown in Figure B-19. Portions of leaves may not show injury because the area has been protected or shaded by other leaves. For example, it is common for one tobacco leaf to lay on a portion of a second leaf thus preventing injury development. The extreme leaf margins also frequently remain free from injury; however, when the injury is bifacial the margins may be most severely injured. This can result in a pinched appearance as the rest of the leaf continues to grow. Cereals and grasses often show injury in the area where the leaf bends.

Injury is usually interveinal since veins are relatively resistant to ozone and develop symptoms only when injury is severe. Large veins remain green even after most of the other leaf tissue has collapsed. Figures B-3, B-9, B-12, and B-15 show typical interveinal injury. However, lesions frequently become concentrated along the sides of large veins and mild upper-surface injury often develops over small veinlets forming a reticulate pattern. Figures B-5, B-13, B-14, B-21, and B-22 show some tendency for concentration of injury along veins.

Leaf maturity. Leaves ranging from about 65-95% of their full size have been reported to be most sensitive to ozone injury.[18,26] Young leaves are resistant, but mature leaves may or may not be resistant, depending on the species. The number of leaves injured during a single exposure to ozone depends on the concentration of ozone and the stage of growth of the plant. In the field older leaves often show injury because they were exposed to ozone during their sensitive stage of development. Mature tissue of species such as beans and pine can be injured by long-term exposure to ozone. For example, ponderosa pine needles usually develop most of their injury after they are mature. Second year needles, therefore, show much more injury than current year needles (Figure B-27). Also injury first develops on the tips of mature needles and slowly progresses towards the base (Figure B-30).

Generally, young plants are most sensitive to ozone and mature plants are relatively resistant. For example, certain extremely sensitive varieties of sweet corn are seldom injured after the plants have reached a height of about 45 cm. Younger cereal and spinach plantings often develop much more injury than mature plantings. Since crops such as sweet corn and spinach are usually planted sequentially, injury development on plants in different stages of growth may be compared.

Symptoms on Selected Species

Symptoms of ozone injury to several selected species or groups of species are discussed briefly as examples.

Spinach. Ozone injury symptoms on spinach range from mild chlorotic mottling of the upper leaf surface through upper-surface bleaching to necrotic collapse of most of the leaf (Figure B-11). Bifacial necrotic spots are frequently limited to randomly scattered areas where the more general upper-surface injury has penetrated the leaf, although sometimes they may be the only symptom. Interveinal, upper-surface necrotic bleaching, which may form a punctate pattern, is most common. The injured areas tend to be much larger than those for most species. Usually lesions range from dull white to tan, but occasionally an upper-surface glazed, pearly appearance or light green to light yellow upper-surface chlorosis develops. Injured leaves frequently become senescent and the symptoms are often inconspicuous 2-3 weeks after they have developed. On very small plants, injury may be limited to cotyledons.

Alfalfa. Symptoms of ozone injury to alfalfa are extremely variable and upper-surface necrosis, bifacial necrosis and chlorosis are all common. Bifacial necrosis may be limited to interveinal, basal, tip, margin areas, or almost any portion of the leaf. White or light yellow-green necrotic areas tend to concentrate between the larger veins. Upper-surface necrotic bleaching may be white, silver-gray, or tan and frequently the injury is concentrated along the larger and secondary veins causing the light-colored veins to stand out against the green background. Sometimes the tissue directly above the vein is injured, but more frequently injury occurs immediately adjacent to the vein. Primary lesions are usually bounded by the smallest veins, resulting in small punctate lesions on the upper surface. Severe injury may also be observed on the lower surface. Light green or light yellow-green chlorosis may extend over much of the leaf with sharply defined small islands of normal green tissue scattered throughout the chlorotic areas (Figure B-17).

Beans. Ozone usually causes either pigmented or bleached lesions which result in bronzing of the upper leaf surface and pods of beans.[27] Also yellowing and abscission of leaves and young pods may develop after exposure to high levels of ozone (Figure B-14). Somewhat darker lesions usually develop on primary leaves rather than on the first trifoliate leaves of young plants. Early senescence of unifoliate leaves after 3-days exposure to 5 pphm ozone has been reported.[28]

Tobacco. Ozone injury to tobacco, which was first known as weather fleck,[29] is generally characterized by numerous small lesions, primarily on the upper leaf surface of fully expanded leaves (Figure B-15). Bifacial lesions are common on the most sensitive varieties, such as Bel-W3.[30] Otherwise, symptomatology may vary, according to the variety or type of tobacco.[31] Leaves exhibit wilting or have an oily appearance on days when the ozone concentration is high. The next morning, water-soaked lesions are a common first symptom, especially if the lower leaf surface is examined with transmitted light before the dew dries. Necrotic lesions usually show a dark color at first, but they change to a light gray or tan fleck as the tissue dries. Under conditions of low nitrogen supply, the lesions may remain dark. Successive periods of air pollution cause new lesions to appear on healthy tissue of recently injured leaves, as well as on fully expanded leaves higher on the stem. Because of the absence of an abscission layer, the dead leaves of tobacco remain attached to the stem.

Lesion size depends on the ozone dosage, variety, and environmental factors,[19] but typical lesions are less than 2 mm in diameter and rounded or irregular in outline. On Bel-W3, the lesions may be bifacial and 6 mm or more in diameter. Microscopic examination of leaves soon after injury reveals changes in the shape of plastids.[31] As breakdown continues, the cell protoplast contracts centrally permitting collapse of the cell wall. The collapse of several palisade cells is reflected in a reciprocal collapse of cells of the upper epidermis. Premature senescence of leaves, including yellowing, is also associated with injury by ozone. Lesions are absent on intensely shaded areas of leaves, as

beneath a fold of a leaf or where a leaf is overlapped by another leaf.

Cereals. Small grains and forage grasses usually develop fine chlorotic or white to tan necrotic lesions between the large veins when injured by ozone (Figures B-18 and B-28). Interveinal streaks or oblong spots frequently develop. Palisade cells are lacking and mild superficial lesions develop on either leaf surface with more severe injury extending completely through the leaf. The outer mesophyll cells adjacent to the vascular bundle sheath, and cells overlying small vascular strands without bundle sheath extensions, are frequently those most readily injured by ozone.[5] The smallest veins are often affected as well as interveinal tissue. Injury is usually concentrated at the apex of a bend. Bifacial necrosis extending across the leaf or part of the leaf is common and, in this case, even the larger veins may be killed. Necrosis is frequently most severe at the leaf tips and margins on seedlings.

Dull gray-green water-soaked areas which develop rapidly into light tan to white bifacial necrotic areas or streaks are a common symptom on sweet corn (Figure B-24). Margins and ends of the necrotic areas may or may not have a chlorotic transition zone. Necrotic areas which develop from a single ozone exposure are usually limited to a 5-13 cm section of the blade. The individual irregular-shaped streaks or areas are relatively large, frequently including the larger veins. The midrib is seldom injured, and there is a tendency for the margins to be most severely injured. A more fine-textured injury is common on certain sweet corn varieties. Smaller, silver-gray to light tan necrotic areas, which may or may not be limited to one leaf surface, often develop in a band across the leaf. If injury develops on several different days, much of the leaf may develop lesions (Figure B-19). Young plants up to about 45 cm in height are usually most sensitive.

Deciduous trees and shrubs. Ozone injury to deciduous trees and shrubs is shown in Figures B-2 thru B-7, B-20 thru B-23, and B-25. Injury is limited more to the upper surface than with annuals, and pigmented and bleached lesion types are most common. When examined with a hand lens, individual lesions normally stand out as small, discrete islands of pigmented, chlorotic, or necrotic tissue. Pigmented lesions are usually bounded by the smallest veins (Figures B-3 thru B-5). Bleached lesions can range from coarse to fine pin-point dots. The concentration of lesions may range from sparse (Figure B-3) to dense (Figure B-2). Lesions may be light brown, reddish-brown, dark brown, black, purple, gray, white, light green or straw colored. Dense lesions may give an overall bronzed, silvery or purple appearance to the upper leaf surface (Figures B-7, and B-20 thru B-23). Chlorotic lesions, which may be just a light shade of green, sometimes develop as the only symptom and for species such as aspen, bifacial injury is common (Figure B-25). Leaves may show little injury initially and then develop a general chlorosis a few days after the ozone exposure. Premature leaf drop is usually associated with this type of chlorosis. Leaf curling and marginal and tip drying have been reported on lilac.[32]

Eastern white pine. Eastern white pine trees affected by ozone or ozone-related pollution complexes may display two types of injury symptoms on their foliage. These symptoms are described as "ozone injury" and "chlorotic dwarf". Symptoms of "semi-mature-tissue needle blight" (SNB)[33] of eastern white pine, a disease that is not caused by ozone, are discussed in the next section. An ozone-induced tip necrosis on the new needles of eastern white pine was first called "emergence tipburn"[9] and later, symptoms ranging from chlorotic flecks through chlorotic mottling, to a severe tip necrosis were labeled "ozone injury" of eastern white pine.[10,14,34]

Costonis[10] described the initial macroscopic symptoms of

ozone injury as minute, silver flecks radiating from the stomata of current-year needles. These tiny silvery flecks, which are best seen under magnification, develop into larger chlorotic flecks visible to the naked eye. Semi-mature tissue is the most seriously affected portion of the needle, but the immature and the mature tissues are often simultaneously affected. Chlorotic flecks may develop into pink lesions and bands followed by a distally spreading, orange-red necrosis which may take 1-2 weeks to reach the needle tips (Figure B-26). On less sensitive trees only chlorotic flecks and mottling may occur, whereas severe needle tip necrosis occurs on more sensitive trees. Microscopically, mesophyll cells adjacent to the stomata are the first to be affected, and endodermis and stele are the last to be affected. New, rapidly growing needles (from about 1 week after emergence until 6 weeks of age) are most sensitive. Normally, 3 years of needle ages occur on eastern white pine. However, on ozone-sensitive trees, the older needles become prematurely senescent and discolored, being cast by mid-summer leaving only the current-year needles.

The chlorotic dwarf disease affecting eastern white pine has been observed for 60 years.[35] Etiological studies by Dochinger et al.[36,37] demonstrated that air pollution, of which ozone forms a part, is the primary casual agent of the disease. The symptoms have been described by Dochinger.[11]

On genetically susceptible trees, the current-year needles emerge normally but not long after they have attained some growth, their natural green color becomes spotted with chlorotic flecks and mottling (Figure B-29). The older foliage turns prematurely yellow and is shed before the current needles reach full development. In final stages, particularly following a drought, the affected current-year needles may develop tipburn.

The disease occurs most commonly on young pines in plantations, and severely affected trees usually succumb before they reach 15 years of age. White pines vary considerably in their susceptibility to chlorotic dwarf, with less sensitive trees exhibiting mild mottling symptoms on near-normal length needles, whereas more sensitive trees exhibit severe stunting of all plant parts and yellow mottled, possibly curled, needles of the current-year.

Ponderosa Pine. The chlorotic decline of ponderosa pine trees in the San Bernardino Mountains of southern California has also been called "X-disease"[38] and "ozone needle mottle".[39] Miller et al.[13,24] have demonstrated that photochemical oxidant smog drifting into the forests from urban areas on the Pacific coast is responsible for the chlorotic decline of ponderosa pine. Extreme variation in susceptibility to chlorotic decline was found in the forest with dead and dying trees growing alongside visibly unaffected trees.

Chronic ozone exposure causes chlorotic needle mottle symptoms which develop from the tip to the base on older needles (Figure B-30). The chlorotic mottle symptoms are eventually followed by a necrotic tip dieback. The oldest needles become prematurely senescent with the chlorotic areas coalescing and turning to a uniform tan color. Normally, 3-5 year old needles occur on ponderosa pine. However, on affected trees the oldest needles are abscissed early, leaving the chlorotic mottled 1 year old needles on the tree during the summer months (Figure B-27).

Symptoms Resembling Injury by Ozone

The physiogenic disease, semimature-tissue needle blight (SNB) of eastern white pine, affects current-year needles only and the symptoms resemble those caused by ozone injury.[12,40] There is, however, some difference between SNB

and ozone injury of eastern white pine. The ozone-sensitive trees usually display chlorotic fleck and mottle in addition to distal reddening following exposure to elevated concentrations of ozone. In SNB-susceptible trees, the symptoms are typically expressed by a distal reddening only, which can occur during periods of normal levels of ambient concentrations of atmospheric ozone. Histological examination of ozone-injury symptoms show mesophyll cell collapse occurring simultaneously in different stages of needle tissue maturation, although it is most pronounced in semimature tissue. In SNB, mesophyll cell collapse initiates only in semimature tissue, which has been defined for the purpose of this disease to be the location in the needle where suberization of the endodermal cells is proceeding. The initial SNB injury occurs macroscopically on stomata-bearing faces as faint pinkish spots in semimature tissue (about 3 weeks old). The spots develop into orange-red bands which spread distally through adjacent, more mature tissue, reaching the needle tips in a period of a few days (Figure B-31). Microscopically, the initiation of SNB occurs in mesophyll cells which are in that stage of needle tissue maturation where suberization of the transverse and radial walls of the endodermal cells is proceeding. Current-year needles possess semimature tissue from about 3 weeks after emergence until about 12 weeks of age, and thus are susceptible to blighting for a period of about 9 weeks.

Various disorders may produce symptoms on other species similar to those produced by ozone. Certain sucking insects, such as mites and leaf hoppers, produce injuries which could be confused with ozone injury. If the injury is caused by insects, careful examination will usually reveal the presence of live insects, or portions of dead ones, especially on the lower leaf surface. In contrast to the effect of high levels of ozone, mites and similar feeding insects tend to empty the palisade cells rather than just causing their collapse. The distribution of insect injury on the leaf surface also tends to be less uniform than that caused by ozone. Certain virus diseases, such as tobacco etch, produce injury patterns which are similar to ozone injury, but chlorosis and mottling of younger leaves in the top of the plant will suggest the presence of a virus. Soils with high soluble manganese may produce symptoms on leaves resembling ozone injury. Radiation-type frost can cause upper surface bleaching of leaf tissue, and moisture stress caused by hot, dry winds can cause bifacial necrosis which may resemble ozone injury.

Chlorine can cause injury to plants that is indistinguishable from injury caused by ozone. Since chlorine injury is almost always associated with pollution from a point source and ozone pollution is more general, the distribution of injury over a large area will indicate which pollutant is involved. Several other air pollutants occasionally cause symptoms resembling ozone injury. Ozone symptom development on alfalfa is so variable that many pollutants can cause a similar response making reliable diagnosis of ozone injury on alfalfa extremely difficult.

Chlorine injury to plants is rare and symptoms caused by most other factors generally resemble ozone injury only superficially. An experienced investigator can usually diagnose ozone injury to most species with a relatively high degree of confidence.

Acknowledgment

This project was supported in part by a grant from the National Air Pollution Control Administration, Consumer Protection and Environmental Health Services, U. S. Department of Health, Education, and Welfare, AP-00452.

References

1. Middleton, J. T., Kendrick, J. B., and Schwalm, H. W., "Injury to herbaceous plants by smog or air pollution," *Plant Disease Reptr.,* **34**, 245-252 (1950).
2. Richards, B. L., Middleton, J. T., and Hewitt, W. B., "Air pollution with relation to agronomic crops: V. oxidant stipple to grape," *Agron. J.,* **50**, 559-561 (1968).
3. Heggestad, H. E. and Middleton, J. T., "Ozone in high concentrations as a cause of tobacco leaf injury," *Science,* **129**, 208-210 (Jan. 1959).
4. Daines, R. H., Leone, I. A., and Brennan, E. G., "Air pollution and its effects on agriculture in New Jersey," *New Jersey Agr. Exp. Sta. Bull.,* **794**, 1-14 (1960).
5. Hill, A. C., Pack, M. R., Treshow, M., Downs, R. F., and Transtrum, L. G., "Plant injury induced by ozone," *Phytopathology,* **51**:6, 356-363 (June 1961).
6. Taylor, O. C., Stephens, E. R., Darley, E. E., and Cardiff, E. A., "Effects of airborne oxidants on leaves of pinto bean and petunia," *Proc. Am. Soc. Hort. Sci.,* **75**, 435-444 (1960).
7. Ledbetter, M. C., Zimmerman, P. W., and Hitchcock, A. E., "The histopathological effects of ozone on plant foliage," *Contrib. Boyce Thompson Inst.,* **20**:4, 275-282 (Oct., Dec. 1959).
8. Engle, R. L., Gableman, W. H., and Romanowski, R. R., "Tip-burn, an ozone incited response in onion, *Allium cepa L.,*" *Proc. Am. Soc. Hort. Sci.,* **86**, 468-474 (1965).
9. Berry, C. R. and Ripperton, L. A., "Ozone, a possible cause of white pine emergence tipburn," *Phytopathology,* **53**, 552-557 (May 1963).
10. Costonis, A. C., "Relationship of ozone, *Lophodermium pinastri,* and *Pullularia pullulans* to needle blight of eastern white pine," *Ph.D. Thesis,* Cornell University, Ithaca, N. Y. (1968).
11. Dochinger, L. S., "The impact of air pollution on eastern white pine: the chlorotic dwarf disease," *J. Air Pollution Control Assoc.,* **18**, 814-816 (1968).
12. Linzon, S. N., "Ozone damage and semimature-tissue needle blight of eastern white pine," *Can. J. Botany,* **45**, 2047-2061 (Dec. 1967).
13. Miller, P. R., Parmeter, J. R., Jr., Taylor, O. C., and Cardiff, E. A., "Ozone injury to the foliage of *Pinus ponderosa,*" *Phytopathology,* **53**, 1072-1076 (1963).
14. Costonis, A. C. and Sinclair, W. A., "Ozone injury to *Pinus strobus,*" *J. Air Pollution Control Assoc.,* **19**, 867-872 (1969).
15. Parmeter, J. R. Jr., Bega, R. V., and Neff, T., "A chlorotic decline of ponderosa pine in southern California," *Plant Disease Reptr.,* **46**, 269-273 (April 1962).
16. Hill, A. C., unpublished data.
17. Menser, H. A. and Heggestad, H. E., "Ozone and sulphur dioxide synergism: injury to tobacco plants," *Science,* **153**, 424-425 (July 1966).
18. Ting, I. P. and Dugger, W. M., Jr., "Factors affecting ozone sensitivity and susceptibility of cotton plants," *J. Air Pollution Control Assoc.,* **18**, 810-813 (1968).
19. Heck, W. W., "Factors influencing expression of oxidant damage to plants," *Ann. Rev. Phytopathology,* **6**, 165-188 (1968).
20. Macdowall, F. D. H., "Predisposition of tobacco to ozone damage," *Can. J. Plant Sci.,* **45**:1, 1-11 (Jan. 1965).
21. Engle, R. L. and Gabelman, W. H., "Inheritance and mechanism of resistance to ozone damage in onion, *Allium cepa L.,*" *Proc. Am. Soc. Hort. Sci.,* **89**, 423-430 (1966).
22. Taylor, O. C., Dugger, W. M., Jr., Thomas, M. D., and Thompson, C. R., "Effect of atmospheric oxidants on apparent photosynthesis of citrus trees," *Plant Physiol. Suppl.,* **36**, XVII (abstract) (1961).
23. Hill, A. C. and Littlefield, N., "Ozone: effect on apparent photosynthesis, rate of transpiration, and stomatal closure in plants," *Environ. Sci. Technol.,* **3**:1, 52-56 (Jan. 1969).
24. Miller, P. R., Parmeter, J. R., Flick, B. H. and Martinez, C. W., "Ozone dosage response of ponderosa pine seedlings," *J. Air Pollution Control Assoc.,* **19**:6, 435-438, (1969).
25. Koukol, J. and Dugger, W. M., Jr., "Anthocyanin formation as a response to ozone and smog treatment in *Rumex crispus L.,*" *Plant Physiol.,* **42**:7, 1023-1024 (July 1967).
26. Bennett, J. H., "Effects of ozone on leaf metabolism," *Ph.D. Thesis,* University of Utah, Salt Lake City, Utah (1969).
27. Weaver, G. M. and Jackson, H. O., "Relationship between bronzing in white beans and phytotoxic levels of atmospheric ozone in Ontario," *Can. J. Plant Sci.,* **48**, 561-568 (Nov. 1968).
28. Engle, R. L. and Gableman, W. H., "The effects of low levels of ozone on pinto beans, *Phaseolus vulgaris L.,*" *Proc. Am. Soc. Hort. Sci.,* **91**, 304-309 (1967).
29. Heggestad, H. E., "Ozone as a tobacco toxicant," *J. Air Pollution Control Assoc.,* **16**:12, 691-694 (Dec. 1966).
30. Heggestad, H. E. and Menser, H. A., "Leaf spot sensitive tobacco strain Bel-W3, a biologic indicator of the air pollutant ozone," *Phytopathology,* **52**, 735 (Abstr.) (Aug. 1962).
31. Burk, L. G. and Heggestad, H. E., "Weather fleck on *Nicotiana tabacum,*" *Plant Disease Reptr.,* **40**:5, 424-427 (May 1956).
32. Hibben, C. R. and Walker, J. T., "A leaf roll-necrosis complex of lilacs in an urban environment," *Proc. Am. Soc. Hort. Sci.,* **89**, 636-642 (1966).
33. Linzon, S. N., "Histological studies of symptoms in semimature-tissue needle blight of eastern white pine," *Can J. Botany,* **45**, 133-143 (1967).
34. Sinclair, W. A. and Costonis, A. C., "Ozone injury to eastern white pine," *Arborist's News,* **32**, 49-52 (1967).
35. Spaulding, P., "The present status of the white pine blights," *U. S. Dept. Agri. Bur. Plant Ind. Circ.,* **35**, 1-12 (1909).
36. Dochinger, L. S., and Seliskar, C. E., "Results from grafting chlorotic dwarf and healthy eastern white pine," *Phytopathology,* **55**, 404-407 (1964).
37. Dochinger, L. S., Seliskar, C. E., and Bender, F. W., "Etiology of chlorotic dwarf of eastern white pine," *Phytopathology,* **55**, 1055 (1965).
38. Asher, J. E., "Observations and theory on *X*-disease or needle dieback," unpublished report to Arrowhead Ranger District, San Bernardino National Forest (1956).
39. Richards, B. L., Sr., Taylor, O. C., and Edmunds, G. F., Jr., "Ozone needle mottle of pine in southern California," *J. Air Pollution Control Assoc.,* **18**, 73-77 (Feb. 1968).
40. Linzon, S. N., "Damage to eastern white pine by sulphur dioxide, semimature-tissue needle blight, and ozone." *J. Air Pollution Control Assoc.,* **16**, 140-144 (March 1966).
41. Heggestad, H. E., unpublished data.
42. Heck, W., personal communication.
43. Brennan, E. and Leone, I. A., "Is variety a key to plant damage in N. J. from ozone?" *New Jersey Agr.,* 13-14 (Jan., Feb. 1966).
44. Sechler, D. and Davis, D. R., "Ozone toxicity in small grain," *Plant Disease Reptr.,* **48**:12, 919-922 (Dec. 1964).
45. Noble, W., "Smog damage to plants," *"Lasca Leaves,* **15**:1, 1-24 (Jan. 1965).
46. Harper, K. and Hill, A. C., unpublished data.
47. Feder, W. A. and Campbell, F. J., "Influence of low levels of ozone on flowering of carnations," *Phytopathology,* **58**:7, 1038-1039 (July 1968).

B 6

Figure B-1. Ozone-injured petunia (*Petunia,* sp.) plants showing upper-surface bleaching on left plant and bifacial necrosis on right plant. Plants were exposed simultaneously. (Photo courtesy of D. Tingey.)

Figure B-2. Upper and lower surfaces of ozone-injured ash (*Fraxinus* sp.) leaflets. Coalescence of lesions results in a dense, purple upper surface (upper leaflet) but the lesions only show through faintly on the lower surface (lowest leaflet).

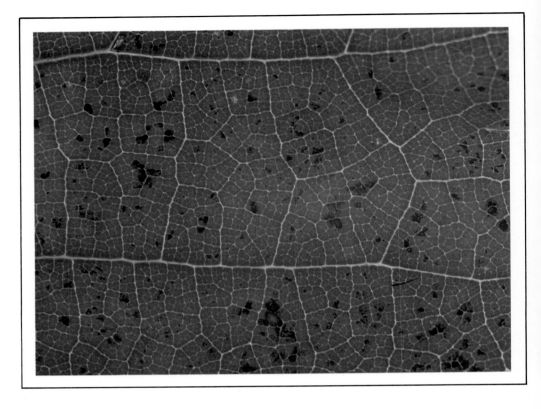

Figure B-3. Close-up of upper surface of ozone-injured grape (*Vitis,* sp.) leaf under reflected light. Dark, pigmented stipple-like lesions develop in palisade tissue between the smallest veins. Coalescence results in larger pigmented areas with uninjured veins running through them.

B 8

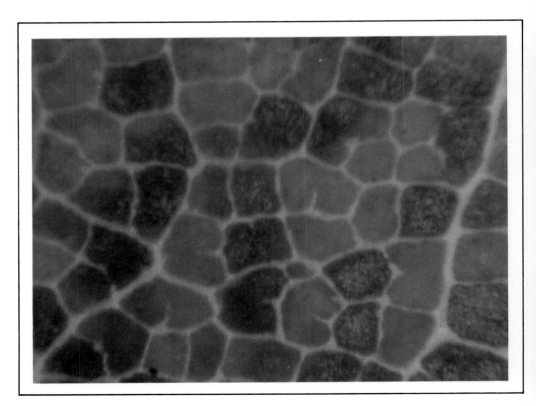

Figure B-4. Close-up of individual ozone-induced lesions on sugar maple (*Acer saccharum,* Marsh.) upper leaf surface under reflected light and 25x magnification. Lesions cover all or part of area between uninjured smallest veins. (Photo courtesy of C. R. Hibben.)

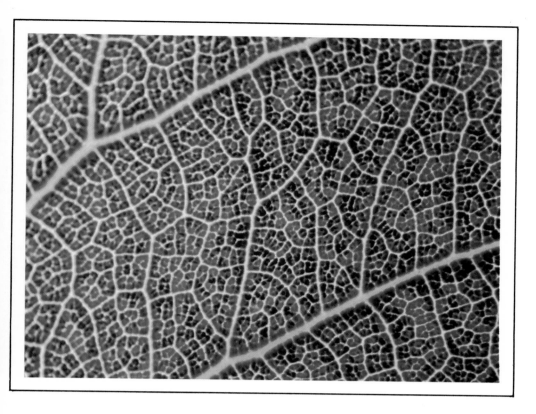

Figure B-5. Portion of ozone-injured apricot (*Prunus armeniaca,* L.) leaf under transmitted light and low magnification. The small, stipple-like lesions bounded by the smallest veins are typical symptoms for most deciduous trees when observed with a hand lens and transmitted light.

B 9

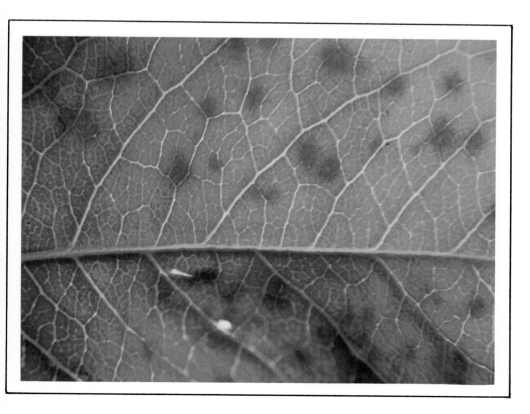

Figure B-6. Close-up of ozone-injured peach (*Prunus persica,* Sieb. & Zucc.) leaf under transmitted light, showing diffusion of red pigments from injured tissue into surrounding tissue and veins.

Figure B-7. Control (right) and ozone-injured (left) sycamore (*Platanus*, sp.) leaves showing reddish-purple pigmentation on the upper leaf surface. Ozone-injured plants are smaller.

B10

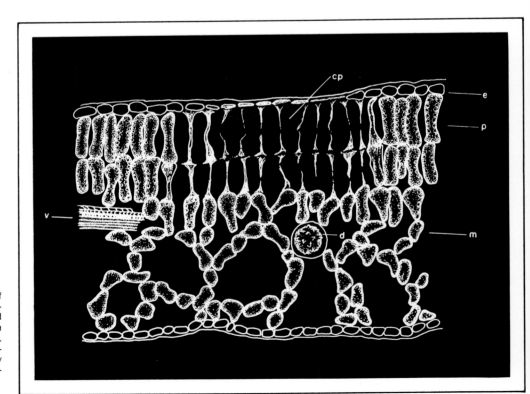

Figure B-8. Cross section of ozone-injured spinach *(Spinacea*, sp.) leaf showing collapsed palisade tissue (cp) over-lain by collapsed epidermal tissue. Also, nucleus (d), normal epidermis (e), palisade (p), spongy mesophyll (m) cells, and a section of vascular strand (v).

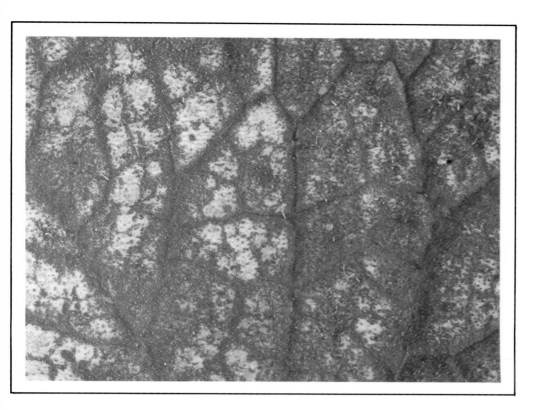

Figure B-9. Close-up of upper surface of ozone-injured pumpkin (*Curcurbita pepo* L.) leaf. Injured palisade and upper epidermis cells result in upper-surface bleaching ranging from small, light-colored flecks to small islands of green tissue in large bleached areas.

B11

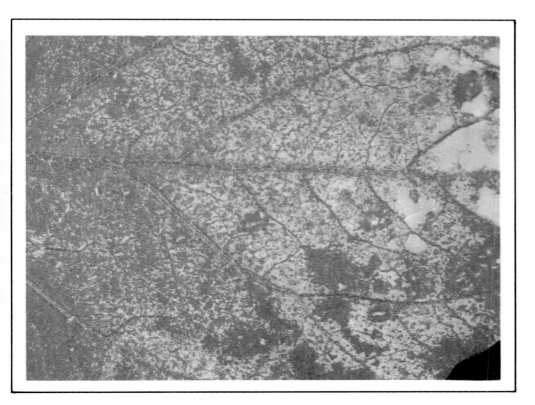

Figure B-10. Close-up of upper surface of ozone-injured eggplant (*Solanum melongena* L.) leaf. Light tan, bifacial necrotic areas are evident towards the tip, and small interveinal bleached areas cover much of the remaining surface.

Figure B-11. Upper surface of ozone-injured spinach (*Spinacea*, sp.) leaves. Large bifacial necrotic areas are evident on top half of left leaf and relatively large upper-surface bleached areas on center and right leaves.

B12

Figure B-12. Ozone-induced bifacial necrosis and upper-surface bleaching of pumpkin (*Curcurbita pepo*, L.) leaf. Larger veins tend to remain green even when injury is severe.

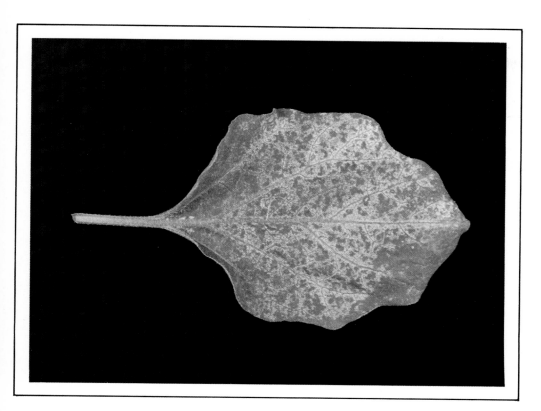

Figure B-13. Upper surface of ozone-injured eggplant (Solanum melongena, L.) leaf. Bleached areas tend to concentrate adjacent to the larger veins, and extreme margins are often free of injury.

B 13

Figure B-14. Ozone-injured bean (Phaseolus, sp.) leaf showing brown necrotic lesions on the upper surface and general chlorosis typical of premature senescence.

Figure B-15. Ozone injury of Bel-W3 tobacco (*Nicotiana tabacum*, L.) leaf showing upper-surface and bifacial lesions. Larger veins remain green.

B14

Figure B-16. Close-up of parsnip (*Pastinaca sativa*, L.) leaf showing ozone-induced, small necrotic and chlorotic lesions on upper surface. Injury is limited to palisade and epidermal tissue.

Figure B-17. Ozone-injured alfalfa (*Medicago Sativa*, L.) leaf showing interveinal chlorotic and necrotic bleaching with interdispersed islands of normal green tissue.

B15

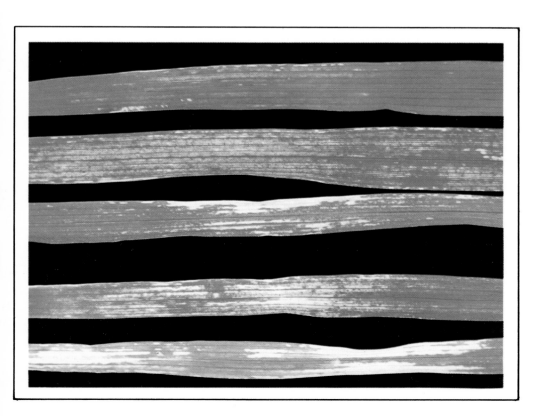

Figure B-18. Ozone-injured oat (*Avena sativa*, L.) leaves showing chlorosis, and single surface and bifacial necrotic bleaching. Injury is frequently limited to a 5-12 cm band across the leaf.

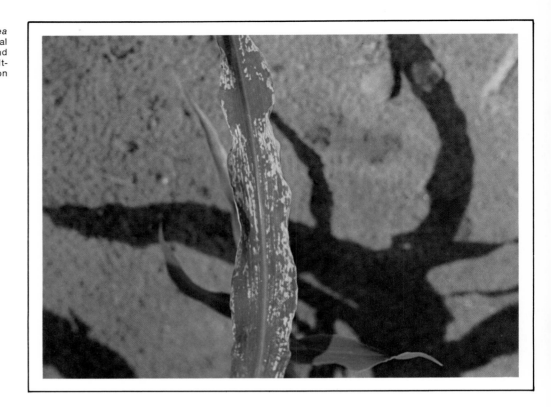

Figure B-19. Sweet corn (*Zea mays,* L.) leaf showing several merging bands of bifacial and upper-surface necrosis resulting from exposure to ozone on several different days.

B16

Figure B-20. Ozone-injury symptoms on American Linden *(Tilia americana,* L.). Dense, small lesions cause a bronzed appearance of upper surface of the mature leaves.

Figure B-21. Ozone-injured crab apple (*Malus baccata*, L.) leaves showing bronzing caused by reddish-brown, necrotic lesions on the upper leaf surface. Leaf on right shows bifacial necrosis.

B 17

Figure B-22. Ozone-induced upper-surface bleaching of older snowberry (*Symphoricarpos albus*, Blake) leaves. Injury is most extensive adjacent to larger veins; extreme leaf margins are free from injury.

Figure B-23. Birch (*Betula*, sp.) leaves showing ozone-induced upper-surface bleaching. The light tan lesions are particularly dense adjacent to the larger veins where injury is almost continuous except for the small veins.

B18

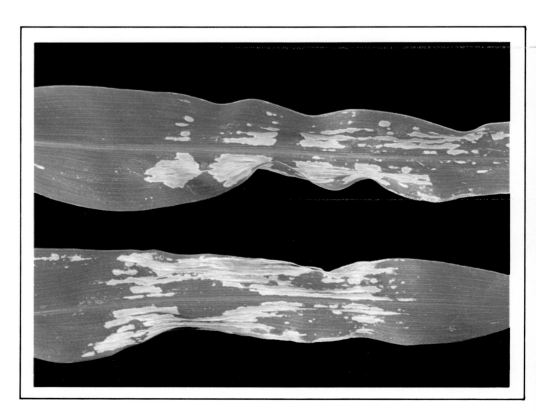

Figure B-24. Ozone injury to sweet corn (*Zea mays*, L.) showing typical tan bifacial necrotic bands across the leaf.

Figure B-25. Ozone-induced, dark-brown bifacial necrotic lesions on aspen (*Populus,* sp.) leaves.

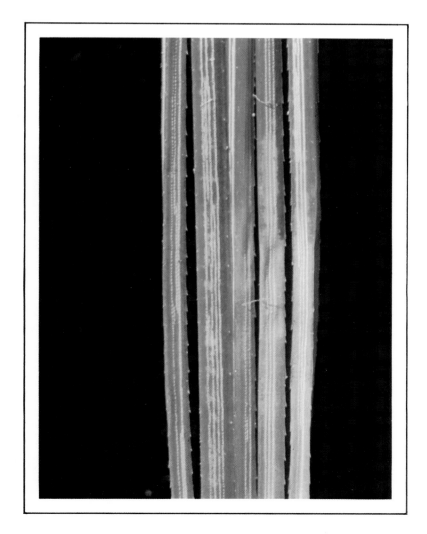

Figure B-26. Ozone injury to five needles from the same fascicle of the current year on eastern white pine (*Pinus strobus,* L.). No injury on needle on left; scattered chlorotic flecks on second needle; lesion in semimature needle tissue developing into a pink band and a tip necrosis in other needles. (Photo courtesy of A. C. Costonis.)

Figure B-27. Ozone injury to ponderosa pine (*Pinus ponderosa,* Laws). Some senescent previous-year needles remaining on two branches, but all have dropped from the third. Light chlorotic mottling on tips of current-year needles. (Photo courtesy of B. L. Richards.)

B 20

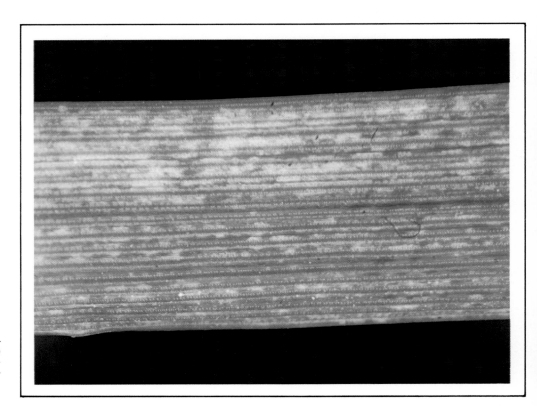

Figure B-28. Close-up of ozone-injured wheat (*Triticum,* sp.) leaf showing chlorotic and necrotic bleached streaks between the larger veins.

Figure B-29. Chlorotic dwarf of eastern white pine (*Pinus strobus*, L.). Chlorotic fleck and mottling on current-year needles. Older needles are cast prematurely. (Photo courtesy of L. S. Dochinger.)

B 21

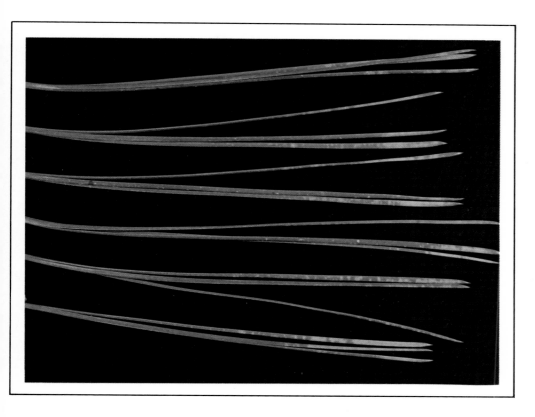

Figure B-30. Chlorotic mottling on tips of ponderosa pine (*Pinus ponderosa*, Laws) needles after exposure to ozone. Mottling continues to progress towards the base of the needle during the second year. (Photo courtesy of B. L. Richards.)

Figure B-31. Semimature-tissue needle blight on eastern white pine (*Pinus strobus*, L.). Initial pink spots in semi-mature needle tissue developing into orange-red bands and a distally spreading tip necrosis on current-year needles.

B 22

Sulfur Dioxide

Thomas W. Barrett
Arizona State University, Tempe, Arizona
and
Harris M. Benedict
Stanford Research Institute, Palo Alto, California

Introduction

More work has been conducted on the response of vegetation to sulfur dioxide than to any other air pollutant. Reviews of the literature have appeared frequently in the past, including those of Thomas[1,2], Thomas and Hendricks[3], Daines[4], Negherbon[5], Brandt and Heck[6], and the Agriculture Research Council of London[7].

Sulfur dioxide is emitted to the atmosphere during the combustion of many fuels, especially coal and petroleum, and in the roasting of sulfide ores during smelting operations. It is also emitted to the atmosphere in regions where active volcanism occurs not only from an active volcano but also from fumeroles and vents that are often found in such areas. The determination of sulfur dioxide is relatively simple and automatic methods of measurement in sub part per million concentrations are available. Because of its ready measurement and stability, it has been possible to establish the concentrations at ground levels which have a probability of producing visible symptoms on vegetation.

Although accurate figures are not available, it is known that significant economic loss in crop yields due to sulfur dioxide does occur annually. In certain agricultural areas, the losses to growers resulting from sulfur dioxide injury are sufficient to be of economic importance and formulae have been devised for estimating the monetary value of these losses. These formulae, for the most part, involve determining the percentage of leaf area that has been injured or destroyed and from these data the resulting crop loss is calculated.[1,8,9]

In addition, there are substantial economic losses to ornamental vegetation used in landscaping, and to forest trees, particularly in coniferous and eastern hardwood type forests.

Markings on vegetation caused by sulfur dioxide are usually found in areas adjacent or close to the source. By contrast, markings due to photochemical air pollutants are often found many miles from industrial or urban sources because the compounds inducing the markings are produced as a result of reactions in the atmosphere.

In the first half of this century large smelting operations were a principal source of the sulfur dioxide that caused injury to vegetation. At the present time emission controls have been installed in many of these smelters so that the emission of several hundred tons of sulfur dioxide per day from these operations is not nearly so common. However, economic losses to certain crops continue in the vicinity of smelters that have not installed proper emission controls for sulfur dioxide or when the emission controls are not operating.

During recent years the consumption of coal and petroleum for heating and power production has increased in urban areas with the result that sulfur dioxide markings on ornamental plantings and home gardens are occurring in urban areas and near large power plants serving municipalities.

Relative Susceptibility

Different species of plants vary widely in their sensitivity to sulfur dioxide when exposed to this gas under conditions most favorable for its absorption by the plant. Studies have been made by several investigators and reviews of their work appear widely in the literature. Thomas[1], Thomas and Hendricks[3], and Negherbon[5], present tables listing a large number of plants under the three categories of sensitive, intermediate, and resistant to sulfur dioxide. From these studies and from personal observations of the authors, the plants shown in Table C-I have been selected as useful indicators of the presence of atmospheric sulfur dioxide on the basis of their wide distribution and relatively high sensitivity to sulfur dioxide. In specific local areas other plants may be found which have high sensitivity and would be useful as indicators.

It should be noted that most trees, with the possible exception of larch, are rated as intermediate to resistant to sulfur dioxide. If the above trees are injured by sulfur dioxide the more sensitive weeds, garden and crop plants in the area should also show injury.

Nearly all varieties of pumpkin and squash that are commonly grown in gardens are very sensitive to sulfur dioxide and will frequently show markings when no other garden plants are marked.

There are so many symptoms that develop on leaves of

TABLE C-I

Selected plants which are relatively sensitive to sulfur dioxide

Crops

Alfalfa *Medicago sativa,* L.	Cotton *Gossypium, sp.,* L.	Soybean *Glycine max.,* Merr.
Barley *Hordeum vulgare,* L.	Oats *Avena sativa,* L.	Wheat *Triticum, sp.*
Bean, field *Phaseolus, sp.,* L.	Rye *Secale cereale,* L.	
Clover *Melilotus & Trifolium, sp.*	Safflower *Carthamus tinctorius,* L.	

Garden Flowers

Aster *Aster bigelovii*	Four o'clock *Mirabilis jalapa,* L.	Verbena *Verbena canadensis,* Brit.
Bachelor's button *Centarea cyanus, L.*	Morning glory *Ipomoea purpurea,* Roth	Violet *Viola, sp.*
Cosmos *Cosmos bipinnatus,* Cau.	Sweet pea *Lathyrus odoratus,* L.	Zinnia *Zinnia elegans,* Lorenz

Trees

Apple *Malus, sp.*	Larch *Larix, sp.*	Pine, Eastern white *Pinus strobus,* L.
Birch *Betula, sp.*	Mulberry *Morus microphylla,* Buckl.	Pine, ponderosa *Pinus ponderosa,* Laws
Catalpa *Catalpa speciosa,* Warder	Pear *Pyrus communis,* L.	Poplar, lombardy *Populus nigra,* L.
Elm, American *Ulmus americana,* L.		

Garden Plants

Bean *Phaseolus vulgaris,* L.	Lettuce *Lactuca sativa,* L.	Spinach *Spinacea oleracea,* L.
Beet, table *Beta vulgaris,* L.	Okra *Hibiscus esculentus,* L.	Squash *Cucurbita maxima,* Duchesne
Broccoli *Brassica oleracea var. botrytis,* L.	Pepper (bell, chili) *Capsicum frutescens,* L.	Sweet Potato *Ipomoea batatas,* Lam.
Brussel sprouts *Brassica oleracea var. gemmifera,* L.	Pumpkin *Cucurbita pepo,* L.	Swiss Chard *Beta vulgaris var. cicla,* L.
Carrot *Daucus carota var. sativa,* L.	Radish *Raphanus sativus,* L.	Turnip *Brassica rapa,* L.
Endive *Cichorium endivia,* L.	Rhubarb *Rheum rhaponticum,* L.	

Weeds

Bindweed *Convolvulus arvensis,* L.	Fleabane *Erigeron canadensis,* L.	Ragweed *Ambrosia artemisiifolia,* L.
Buckwheat *Fagopyrum sagittatum,* Gilib.	Lettuce, Prickly *Lactuca scariola,* L.	Sunflower *Helianthus, sp.*
Careless weed *Amaranthus palmeri,* S. Wats	Mallow *Malva parviflora*	Velvet-weed *Gaura parviflora,* Dougl.
Curly dock *Rumex crispus,* L.	Plantain *Plantago major,* L.	

C 2

plants which resemble those due to sulfur dioxide that no one can truthfully state that he can observe a single leaf, without any additional knowledge, and state that the injury was or is due to sulfur dioxide and to no other agent or factor. The positive identification of sulfur dioxide markings on vegetation can be made only after all foliar symptoms and related evidence have been considered. These include: (1) the presence of suspected sources of sulfur dioxide; (2) the species of plants that develop markings; (3) the type of markings that are observed; (4) the pattern shown by the severity of the markings and locations of occurrence, *i.e.,* most severe near the suspected source on species known to be sensitive and decreasing in severity with distance from that source. This will depend upon the atmospheric conditions prevailing during the period of fumigation.

Mathematical equations expressing the relationship between the duration of exposure and the concentration of sulfur dioxide have been derived from data of limited time exposures that produce markings on plants [1,3,6]. In recent years, workers in Germany [10,11] have presented additional concentration—time equations which seem to give better agreement over a wider range of observations. Although these relations are of value in predicting what might occur under given conditions of a fumigation, they are not readily adaptable to assessing the economic loss sustained by a crop that has been injured by sulfur dioxide.

In general, yields of crops are not affected unless chronic or acute markings have developed on the leaves. Results seem to show that about 5% of the leaf area must be destroyed before the crop yield for such crops as small grains is significantly or measurably reduced. For alfalfa, experiments indicate that if the leaf destruction is of the order of a few percent (less than 5%) there is no residual effect on the yield even after several fumigations.[12]

The estimation of economic loss to crop plants injured by sulfur dioxide is normally accomplished by taking leaf counts of injured leaves at sampling points throughout the field and from these counts estimating the percent leaf area destroyed for the entire crop. From the leaf-count data the loss in yield is calculated using the procedures described in the literature by several investigators [1,3,8,9].

Although this procedure may be applied to most field crops, it will not apply to certain vegetable crops such as lettuce and green onions where the appearance of the leaves is an important factor in determining their marketability. With crops such as these, the monetary loss far exceeds that determined by the leaf area damaged by sulfur dioxide. Nor will it apply to flowers or ornamental plants whose value and beauty lies in the appearance of their foliage as well as their blooms. Experiments have been conducted to study the effects of toxic amount of sulfur dioxide on the photosynthetic process[12,13]. Photosynthesis in alfalfa, which is highly sensitive to sulfur dioxide, was not affected by fumigations with levels up to 0.4 ppm unless the fumigation was continued long enough to produce acute or chronic markings. When visible markings did appear the photosynthetic rate was reduced in proportion to the reduction in the area of photosynthetically active (or uninjured) tissue. When alfalfa was exposed to sulfur dioxide concentrations of 0.5 ppm or above, the rate of photosynthesis was reduced during the exposure but quickly returned to normal when the fumigation ceased, provided that no acute or chronic injury had occurred. If such injury had occurred, the reduction in photosynthesis generally corresponded to the area of photosynthetic tissue that had been killed or otherwise affected[4,12,13]. In other words, no physiological effects unrelated to visible injury have been found as a result of sulfur dioxide fumigations of plants. In recent years, injury without visible symptoms has been ascribed to sulfur dioxide[14,15] but these occurred under conditions where other air pollutants were present, hence, they cannot be positively attributed to sulfur dioxide alone.

Sulfur dioxide has been studied almost exclusively as a single air pollutant. Recently, however, studies have been conducted to determine the effectiveness of other gases or aerosols in the presence of sulfur dioxide in producing plant injury. Menser and Heggestad[16] found that sub-lethal mixtures of ozone (0.037 ppm) and sulfur dioxide (0.24 ppm) produced ozone-like symptoms on leaves of Bel-W3 tobacco after an exposure of 2 hrs. This response was later substantiated and reported by Heck[17], who also states that a similar synergistic response between nitrogen dioxide and sulfur dioxide was found using the same variety of tobacco.

It is important to remember that annual plants vary over a wide range in sensitivity to sulfur dioxide as they grow from the seedling stage to maturity. This factor combined with differences in environmental conditions has led to much confusion over the relative order of sensitivity among various species of plants.

Symptomatology

There is a range of plant markings produced by all air pollutants that visibly affect plants. Some markings are considered to be typical of a given pollutant and are used to identify the pollutant. This is true for sulfur dioxide. There are, however, several agents which produce markings on plants that very closely resemble sulfur dioxide markings (PAN, NO_2, Cl_2, HCl). For this reason, it is necessary to examine several plant species within the area where sulfur dioxide injury is suspected in order to determine with any degree of certainty that sulfur dioxide is actually the causative agent.

Once sulfur dioxide enters the mesophyll tissue of the leaves it is exposed to many physical and chemical processes associated with living organisms. It reacts with water to produce the sulfite ion which is slowly oxidized to the sulfate ion. The sulfate ion may then be utilized by the plant as nutritional sulfur and converted to an organic form[18]. The sulfite and sulfate ions are toxic to plant cells when present in excessive amounts. However, because of its reducing potential, the sulfite ion is estimated to be some 30 times more toxic than the sulfate ion[19].

The accumulation of sulfite in the tissues of the leaves produces two general types of markings designated as chronic markings and acute markings, depending upon the rate of accumulation. If the accumulation rate is slow, the capacity of the cells to oxidize the sulfite ions may never be exceeded and no injury will result until sufficient sulfate accumulates to produce a salt effect. This type of chronic injury is characterized by a general chlorotic appearance of the leaf as illustrated in Figures C-1 and C-2. A similar type of chronic marking usually occurs following a fumigation of relatively short duration due to the accumulation of sulfite at sub-lethal concentrations. Although the cells are not killed there is a bleaching of the chlorophyll which appears as a mild chlorosis or yellowing of the leaf or a silvering or bronzing of the undersurface. Cotton and alfalfa often exhibit undersurface silvering due to a collapse of cells immediately beneath the epidermis. While many plants show an ivory or white type of chronic marking, other plants which have strong red, brown, or black pigments normally concealed by the chlorophyll will exhibit these colors following injury. Note Figures C-3 and C-4 for examples.

Chronic type markings due to sub-lethal concentrations of sulfite appear similar to those due to an excessive accumulation of sulfate. In both cases, the leaf remains turgid and apparently continues to function at a reduced level of efficiency proportional to the extent of the injury. The accumulation of sulfates and reduction in the buffer capacity of the leaf may proceed to a point where the leaf is subjected to a process resembling normal senescence.[7]

Acute injury resulting from the absorption of lethal quantities of sulfur dioxide appears as marginal or intercostal areas of dead tissue which at first have a full grayish-green water-soaked appearance. Upon drying these areas take on a bleached ivory color in most plant species. However, as with the chronic injury, brown, red or black colors may predominate in the injured area. After a period of time, the dead or necrotic areas may fall out leaving a very ragged appearance to the leaf. When the major portion of the leaf is so injured an abscission layer often forms at the base of the petiole and the leaf is shed.

The acute markings produced on pinnately-veined plant leaves consist primarily of irregular necrotic or dead areas between the side veins, often closer to the midrib than to the margin of the leaf as shown in Figures C-7 thru C-15. For palmately-veined leaves, the necrotic areas generally appear closer to the point of branching of the main veins than toward the margin as shown in Figures C-1 and C-16. However the markings on zinnia leaves in Figure C-17 are distributed from the central section to the leaf tip. In certain plants, however, markings first appear at the leaf margin, then extend toward the leaf base as, for example, Ginkgo biloba and often, alfalfa. For most plants, the greater the exposure the closer to the margin the lesions extend until, with severe exposures, the entire leaf may be marked or killed.

The markings that develop on grasses and other monocotyledonous plants such as lilies and gladioli (Gladiolus, sp.) usually occur as necrotic streaks developing from near the tip and extending downward to the base of the leaf alongside the midrib as shown in Figure C-18. With grass leaves such as wheat, oats and barley, which usually bend at some point along the blade, the markings often begin at the bend as illustrated in Figures C-19 and C-20.

Figure C-21 illustrates typical sulfur dioxide markings that occur on needle-leaved plants such as pines, larch and Douglas fir (*Pseudotsuga taxifolia*, Brit.). The markings usually begin at the needle tip and extend toward the base. The degree of extension is related to the severity of the exposure. When successive exposures occur a distinct banding pattern often appears[20]. With moderate exposure to sulfur dioxide the older needles of conifer tend to become chlorotic and are shed prematurely. With exposure to larger dosages, needles develop a water-soaked appearance which soon changes into reddish-brown necrosis of the tip. The necrotic pattern may first appear as bands around the needle with the terminal portion later turning a reddish brown. Seldom is a completely green needle observed in an affected fascicle. The middle-aged needles exhibit the most necrosis, but the older needles are cast first. Expanding needles are rarely injured[12,21,22]. Needles tend to persist on young branches resulting in an absence of needles at the base of branches and at the bottom of the tree. This tendency for older needles to be shed prematurely results in an increasing needle shortage. Such trees make limited growth and may die prematurely[22].

Needletip dieback of conifers can also be caused by fluorides, winter kill, water stress and by herbicides containing boron. The color of boron-killed needles is usually more reddish than the color of the needles killed by other agents, but the symptoms closely resemble each other. Because needles produced in the current growing season are more sensitive than older needles, it is much safer to examine only the current year's needles in looking for or assessing sulfur dioxide effects on needle-bearing plants. Tip necrosis of needles that have gone through a winter can be due to many causes other than sulfur dioxide.

Oats, wheat and barley are fairly sensitive to sulfur dioxide and the tip dieback of leaf blades is a common symptom of injury. However, such tip killing can be produced by many natural causes such as drought, frost and hot weather. Tip dieback is also common on sulfur dioxide-resistant grasses such as corn (*Zea mays* L.), sorghum (*Sorghum vulgare*, Pers.), Johnson grass (*Holcus halepensis*, L.) and many native grasses.

While acute markings on alfalfa are white or ivory in color, these markings may or may not develop in locations considered typical for sulfur dioxide. They may first appear as very narrow streaks near the margin of the leaf or they may develop in the more typical interveinal locations, sometimes at the tips of the leaflets. On very humid or foggy days with just a threshold concentration of sulfur dioxide, the markings may be a dull grayish-green color that is barely noticeable on the upper surface or may appear as only a light silvering on the under surface. Some markings on alfalfa produced by photochemical smog may be confused with those produced by sulfur dioxide.

It is characteristic to find both chronic and acute type markings on many plant species following an exposure to sulfur dioxide. This is an important factor used to identify sulfur dioxide injury in the field as opposed to markings caused by other agents. Often both types of markings may appear on the same leaf as shown in Figures C-1 and C-2.

It is the consensus of opinion that sulfur dioxide enters the leaf tissue by way of the stomata. Thus, factors that affect stomatal opening will affect the response of plants to sulfur dioxide[1,2,4,5,7]. Plants in which stomata close at night are much less sensitive to night fumigations than day fumigations. Conversely, plants whose stomata remain open at

night are sensitive to both night-time and day-time fumigations. Since the stomata of most plants close at night, sulfur dioxide injury to plants results largely from day-time exposures[23,24]. Resistance of plants to sulfur dioxide increases as the soil moisture approaches the wilting point[25]. When the leaves are turgid they are more sensitive than when wilted, since wilted plants are likely to have closed stomata. Thus, moisture stress greatly reduces the sensitivity of plants to sulfur dioxide. Plants are generally more sensitive to sulfur dioxide as the humidity increases, a response possibly due to the effects of humidity on stomatal opening. There is some indication, however, that at very high humidities of 70% or above some factor other than stomatal opening may be operating[19].

Plants have been found to be more susceptible to sulfur dioxide injury when the sugar content of the leaves is low, such as early in the morning as contrasted to afternoon following a photosynthetic period[1].

The younger fully-expanded leaves are usually most sensitive to sulfur dioxide followed by the older leaves, while the enlarging leaves are the last to show injury. This characteristic is illustrated in Figures C-5 and C-6.

Symptoms Resembling Injury by Sulfur Dioxide

There are many symptoms or markings produced on leaves of plants by frost and other weather conditions, diseases, insect pests, spray chemicals and residual herbicides in the soil that may be confused with sulfur dioxide symptoms or symptoms produced by other pollutants. For example, the so-called "white spot" and "tipburn" which develops on alfalfa under certain weather conditions may be confused with sulfur dioxide injury. These symptoms often appear when the plants have been subjected to a period of drought and high temperatures followed by a heavy rainfall or irrigation. This marking may be a white flecking or marginal streaking or yellowing extending from the tip of the leaflet inward. The mechanism by which this marking is produced is not completely understood but is believed to be the result of salt accumulation in the leaf tips from the readily available salts in the soil and associated with the rapid increase in moisture supply. Figures C-22 and C-23 illustrate these symptoms.

Sulfur dioxide-like markings have been observed on cotton and alfalfa plants growing in fields far removed from any atmospheric sources of sulfur dioxide. The temperature of the marked leaves is so much higher than that of unmarked leaves or leaves injured by sulfur dioxide that the difference can actually be felt; this characteristic makes identification and differentiation from sulfur dioxide injury relatively easy. Chemical analysis of such leaves indicates an abnormally high concentration of salts, particularly calcium sulfate. This type of injury has been found on plants growing in soils with a high gypsum content and generally appears on cotton plants that have been subjected to a moisture stress under conditions of high temperatures and low relative humidity. The symptoms usually appear shortly after irrigation following a period of moisture stress and high transpiration rates. The markings most closely resemble acute interveinal sulfur dioxide markings with ivory colored to brown necrotic areas developing. Figure C-24 illustrates this symptom on a cotton leaf.

Anhydrous ammonia escaping from storage tanks or tractor applicators on farms where it is being used as a fertilizer can produce markings which resemble sulfur dioxide injury. Normally such injury is not difficult to identify except where it occurs simultaneously with sulfur dioxide injury. Many factors can produce chlorosis such as iron deficiency, lack of nitrogen, or presence of other pollutants such as fluorides, insect injury and diseases.

References

1. Thomas, M. D., "Effects of air pollution on plants", *Air Pollution, World Health Organ. Monograph Ser.*, **46**, 233-278, Geneva (1961).
2. Thomas, M. D., "Gas damage to plants", *Ann. Rev. Plant Physiol.*, **2**, 293-322 (1951).
3. Thomas, M. D. and Hendricks, R. H., "Effect of air pollution on plants", in *Air Pollution Handbook*, ed. Magil, P.L. *et al.*, section 9, 1-44, McGraw-Hill, New York (1956).
4. Daines, R. H., "Sulfur dioxide and plant response," *J. Occupational Med.*, **10**, 84-92 (1968).
5. Negherbon, W. O., "Sulfur dioxide, sulfur trioxide, and fly ash: their nature and their role in air pollution", *EEI Research Project RP62*, Edison Electric Institute, New York (1966).
6. Brandt, C. S. and Heck, W. W., "Effects of air pollutants on plants", in *Air Pollution,* ed. Stern, A. C., vol. 1, 401-443, Academic Press, New York (1968).
7. Agricultural Research Council, "The effects of air pollution on plants and soils", London (1967).
8. Brisley, H. R. and Jones, W. W., "Sulfur dioxide fumigation of wheat with special reference to its effect on yield", *Plant Physiol.*, **25**, 666-681 (1950).
9. Brisley, J. R., David, C. R., and Booth, J. A., "Sulfur dioxide fumigation of cotton with special reference to its effect on yield", *Agron. J.*, **51**, 77-80 (1959).
10. Guderian, R., Van Haut, H., and Stratmann, H., "Problems of the recognition and evaluation of the effects of gaseous air impurities on vegetation", *Zeit. Pflanzenkrankh. Pflanzenschutz,* **67**, 257-264 (1960).
11. Zahn, R., "The significance of continuous and intermittent sulfur dioxide action for plant reaction", *Staub.*, **23**, 343-352 (1963).
12. National Research Council of Canada, *Effect of sulfur dioxide on vegetation*, 393-428, Ottawa, Canada (1939).
13. Thomas, M. D. and Hill, G. R., "Relation of sulfur dioxide in the atmosphere to photosynthesis and respiration of alfalfa", *Plant Physiol.*, **12**, 309-383 (1937).
14. Bleasdale, J. K. A., "The effect of air pollution on plant growth", *Symp. Inst. Biol.*, **8**, 81-87 (1959).
15. Guderian, R. and Stratmann, H., "Field trials for the determination of sulfur dioxide effects on vegetation. I. Review of experimental techniques and experimental evaluation", *Forschungsber. Landes Nordrhein-Westfalen,* **1118**, 7-102 (1962).
16. Menser, H. A. and Heggestad, H. E., "Ozone and sulfur dioxide synergism: Injury to tobacco plants", *Science*, **153**, 424-435 (1966).
17. Heck, W. W., "Factors influencing expression of oxidant damage to plants", *Ann. Rev. Phytopath.*, **6**, 165-188 (1968).
18. Thomas, M. D., Hendricks, R. H., Bryner, L. C., and Hill, G.R., "A study of the sulfur metabolism of wheat, barley and corn using radioactive sulfur", *Plant Physiol.*, **19**, 227-244 (1944).
19. Thomas, M. D., Hendricks, R. H., Collier, T. R., and Hill, G. R., "The utilization of sulfate and sulfur dioxide for the nutrition of alfalfa", *Plant Physiol.*, **18**, 345-371 (1943).
20. Linzon, S. N., "Sulfur dioxide injury to trees in the vicinity of petroleum refineries", *Forest Chronicle*, **41**, 245-250 (1965).
21. Linzon, S. N., "Damage to eastern white pine by sulfur dioxide, semimature tissue needle blight, and ozone", *J. Air Pollution Control Assoc.*, **16**, 140-144 (1966).
22. Scheffer, T. C., and Hedgcock, G. G., "Injury to northwestern forest trees by sulfur dioxide from smelters", *U.S. Dept. Agric. Tech. Bull.*, 1117 (1955).
23. Katz, M., "Sulfur dioxide in the atmosphere and its relation to plants and soils", *Ind. Eng. Chem.*, **41**, 2450-2465 (1949).
24. Thomas, M. D., Hendricks, R. H., and Hill, G. R., "Sulfur metabolism of plants: effects of sulfur dioxide on vegetation", *Ind. Eng. Chem.*, **42**, 2231-2235 (1950).
25. Zimmerman, P. W. and Crocker, W., "Toxicity of air containing sulfur dioxide gas", *Contrib. Boyce Thompson Inst.*, **6**, 455-470 (1934).

Figure C-1. Chronic sulfur dioxide injury to short staple cotton (*Gossypium,* sp.) leaves. Leaf on left illustrates typical interveinal chlorosis, while leaf on right shows a rare veinal-type chlorosis. Also acute injury in the form of white necrotic patches occurs on the right leaf.

C 6

Figure C-2. Acute and chronic sulfur dioxide injury to alfalfa (*Medicago Sativa,* L.) leaves. Left leaf shows typical acute markings as viewed from top surface. Right leaf is the under surface with acute injury on the center leaflet and underside. Silvering typical of chronic injury appears on the two side leaflets.

Figure C-3. Acute sulfur dioxide injury to the leaves of quince (*Cydonia oblonga*, Mill.). This is one of the most striking examples of the brownish-red coloration which many plants show when injured.

Figure C-4. Acute sulfur dioxide injury to chrysanthemum (*Chrysanthemum*, sp.). This dark brown color of the injured area is also typical of acute sulfur dioxide injury to cockelbur. Chrysanthemum is generally considered to be resistant to sulfur dioxide.

Figure C-5. Typical acute sulfur dioxide injury to yellow summer squash *(Cucurbita pepo,* L.). All squash and pumpkin plants bleach to a white or ivory color in the acutely injured areas. Note that the new top leaves not fully expanded at the time of fumigation were not injured.

C8

Figure C-6. Typical acute markings on the leaves of careless weed *(Amaranthus palmeri,* S. Wats.). Note that the new expanding leaves are resistant to sulfur dioxide.

Figure C-7. Acute sulfur dioxide injury to the pinnately-veined leaves of the garden pea (*Pisum sativum*, L.).

Figure C-8. Acute sulfur dioxide injury to leaves of apricot (*Prunus armeniaca*, L.). The top two leaves show the upper leaf **surface** while the bottom three leaves show the under surface.

Figure C-9. Acute sulfur dioxide injury to rose (*Rosa,* sp.) leaves. The left leaves show the under surface while the right leaves show the upper surface.

C10

Figure C-10. Acute sulfur dioxide injury to mesquite (*Prosopis juliflora,* (Schwartz) De Cand.) leaves. Note that the severity of the injury decreases toward the leaf tip and the tip leaflets show very little injury.

Figure C-11. Acute sulfur dioxide injury to three varieties of oak. Lower left, black jack oak (*Quercus marilandica*, Muench.); center, shumard oak (*Quercus shumardi*, Buckl.); lower right, post oak (*Quercus stellata*, Wangenh.). (Photo courtesy of R. H. Daines and S. C. Stabe.)

Figure C-12. Acute sulfur dioxide injury to marigold (*Tagetes*, sp.). The injured areas quickly dry out, curl up and become very brittle.

Figure C-13. Acute sulfur dioxide injury to peach (*Prunus persica,* Sieb. & Zucc.) leaves. Top leaf shows the upper surface, bottom leaf, the under surface. Often the injury occurs only on one half of the leaf as shown here.

C12

Figure C-14. Acute sulfur dioxide injury to Irish potato leaflets (*Solanum tuberosum,* L.). The upper surface shows a reddish-brown color while the under surface is generally of an ivory color.

Figure C-15. Acute sulfur dioxide injury to pecan (*Carya pecan*, Engelm. & Graebn.) leaves. The left leaf shows the upper surface while the other two leaves show the under surface. Note that the dark brownish-black color is nearly the same on both surfaces. Broadbeans (*Phaseolus*, sp.) and a few other plants also show this dark coloration when injured.

Figure C-16. Typical acute sulfur dioxide injury to sweet potato (*Ipomoea batatas*, Lam.) leaves. Left leaf shows the upper surface while the right leaf shows the under surface.

Figure C-17. Acute sulfur dioxide injury to zinnia (*Zinnia,* sp.) leaves. Right leaf shows the upper surface and the other two leaves show the under surface.

C14

Figure C-18. Acute injury to gladiolus (*Gladiolus,* sp.) experimentally fumigated with a sulfur dioxide concentration of 1.5 ppm for 2 days. (Photo courtesy of L. H. Weinstein.)

Figure C-19. Acute sulfur di-oxide injury to Sonora wheat (*Triticum*, sp.). Most grasses typically show an ivory color in the injured areas.

C 15

Figure C-20. Acute sulfur di-oxide injury to grain sorghum (*Sorghum vulgare,* Pers.). Both sorghum and corn (*Zea mays,* L.) are considered to be re-sistant to sulfur dioxide. In this experimental fumigation, the sorghum was interplanted with cotton. The cotton leaves were severely injured by the 15 ppm of sulfur dioxide fumigation for 30 min.

Figure C-21. Typical acute sulfur dioxide to loblolly pine (*Pinnus taeda,* L.). (Photo courtesy of R. H. Daines and S. C. Stabe.)

C16

Figure C-22. "White spot" physiological disorder of alfalfa (*Medicago sativa,* L.). Top row shows upper surfaces of leaves while bottom row is the under surfaces. Note the general similarity to acute sulfur dioxide injury.

Figure C-23. "Tipburn" physiological disorder of alfalfa (*Medicago sativa*, L.). Occasionally sulfur dioxide will mark leaves in a similar manner but the black line between injured and uninjured areas will not be present.

Figure C-24. Cotton (*Gossypium*, sp.) leaf showing injury similar to acute sulfur dioxide injury but in this case was caused by an abnormally high uptake and concentration of sulfate from soluble gypsum in the irrigation water.

Fluoride

Michael Treshow
University of Utah, Salt Lake City, Utah
and
Merrill R. Pack
Washington State University, Pullman, Washington

Introduction

The hazards of fluoride to vegetation have been recognized since late in the 19th century[1], but losses to agriculture and forestry from fluoride have greatly increased since the second world war with the vast expansions of industries that are major users of materials high in fluoride. Fluoride is wide-spread in the earth's crust as a natural component of soil, rocks, and minerals such as apatite, cryolite, topaz and micas and hornblendes.[2] When these materials are heated to high temperatures, or treated with acid during industrial processing, toxic quantities of fluoride may be released into the atmosphere. Fluoride also is evolved from a wide variety of industrial processes in which fluorine compounds are utilized as catalysts or fluxes, and from burning fuels and waste. The production of aluminum, steel, ceramics, and phosphorus chemicals and fertilizers are examples of manufacturing sources that may emit significant quantities of fluoride. The amount of fluoride released into the atmosphere from a particular source may range from a few pounds to several thousand pounds per day, depending on the volume of production and the amount of fluoride in the raw materials, fluxes, or fuels.

The economic significance of fluoride effects on vegetation is rarely certain. Visible symptoms on plants around fluoride sources are frequently confined to a few sensitive plant species in limited areas, and the significance will depend on the prevalence and importance of these susceptible species. Most of the potential sources of large quantities of fluoride have installed emission control equipment that greatly reduces emissions, or have constructed tall stacks to allow fluoride to disperse before it reaches ground level. These control measures have appreciably reduced, or eliminated many previously serious fluoride pollution situations. However, some problems still exist where fluoride concentrations in forage are high or leaf markings are observed on sensitive species.

Economic loss may be notable, even in the absence of any leaf markings, when fluoride concentrations in pasture grasses, alfalfa, or other forage crops become sufficiently high to render the crop unuseable unless it is mixed with low-fluoride hay.

Where plant leaves have been severely marked by fluoride, it is often assumed that growth and production have been reduced in relative proportion to the percentage of the total leaf area that has been destroyed or rendered nonfunctional. However, the accuracy of this assumption depends in part on when the injury occurs. If plants are exposed to fluoride late in the growing season, it may have little effect on the growth of the plant. If the marketed portion of a plant is visibly affected, as may occur with peach fruit or the bracts of gladiolus flowers, the economic loss may be great in relation to the amount of actual injury. Aesthetic losses associated with visible injury to ornamental plants are even more difficult to evaluate.

Much of the uncertainty about the economic significance of fluoride injury to plants hinges on whether or not fluoride reduces plant growth or production by interfering with the metabolism of tissues that are not visibly marked. Such effects have been demonstrated in controlled fumigation experiments, usually under rather severe treatments with hydrogen fluoride.[6-10] Some instances of apparent growth stimulation by low concentrations of fluoride have also been observed,[10-12] as have some genetic effects.[13] Further research is needed to substantiate the subtle physiological effects of fluoride before their occurrence and importance under field conditions can be reliably appraised.

Accumulation

Fluoride released into the atmosphere occurs in various chemical and physical forms, and its toxicity to vegetation depends on how readily it is absorbed into the plant tissue. Gaseous compounds such as hydrogen fluoride and silicon tetrafluoride probably are mainly responsible for fluoride injury to vegetation. Particulate materials such as calcium fluoride and cryolite dust are deposited on leaf surfaces where they have little effect on the plant and are easily washed off by rain. The possibility of injury is greatest when the particulate fluoride is soluble, because it may dissolve in moisture on the leaf surfaces and then be absorbed into the tissue.

Fluoride injury to vegetation commonly results from gradual accumulation of fluoride in the plant tissue over a period of time. Therefore, the duration of exposure, as well as the atmospheric concentrations, are important in determining the severity of injury. Symptom expression, however, is not always related strictly to the fluoride dosage (product of concentration and time) because appreciable amounts are often washed from plant foliage by rain, and in some cases fluoride may be converted within the tissue into forms that are not active in causing injury. Consequently, the severity of leaf markings produced by a short-term exposure to high fluoride concentrations may be high in relation to the total amount of fluoride retained in the leaves at the time they are analyzed. Plants take up some fluoride from the soil, but the amount is generally small and its contribution to plant injury negligible even when the soil fluoride content is relatively high.[1,5]

Relative Susceptibility

Different plant species, varieties or clones of a single variety, and even plants from different seeds lots, differ greatly in their sensitivity or susceptibility to fluoride. Extremely sensitive plants, such as Chinese apricot and certain varieties of gladiolus, may be marked by exposure to hydrogen fluoride concentrations below 0.1 ppb, while most species will show no effects from several times as much fluoride.

It must be stressed that the extent and degree of fluoride injury will depend on many variables. It would be helpful if some air concentration or leaf fluoride content could be associated quantitatively with each of the sensitivity categories, but such a value would be extremely tenuous. Too many interrelated factors influence the atmospheric concentration which is toxic, or the foliar fluoride content found when leaf injury first appears.

While investigators would like to relate the degree of injury to atmospheric or foliar fluoride concentrations, no one has yet managed to quantitatively correlate these factors in the field. Possible crop injury and losses can be evaluated only by field observations. The value of knowing the concentration of fluoride in the leaves and air lies mainly in providing an index, or measure, of the presence of fluoride and determining the effectiveness of air pollution control programs.

Plants often are arbitrarily divided into sensitive, intermediate, and resistant categories. The concentration and duration of exposure; the time of year when plants were exposed; the soil moisture regime; the degree of moisture and temperature stress before, during, and after exposure; the form of fluoride present, whether gaseous or particulate; the nutritional status of the plant; age of tissues; and the general plant vigor and genetic sensitivity all influence sensitivity. Presumably, sensitive plants are those that would be injured by low concentrations of fluoride in the air or following accumulation of only small amounts of fluoride. Thomas and Hendricks[14] regarded plants as sensitive which were injured by continuous exposure to 5 ppb or less fluoride for 7-9 days. Adams et al.[15] found that twenty-nine out of thirty-nine species and varieties tested were injured by exposure to 1.5 ppb HF for 8 hrs a day, 5 days a week over an extended period. Far too little work has been conducted to definitely establish quantitative relations between air levels and sensitivity for most species.

A list of some common plant species, which are relatively sensitive to fluoride, based on fumigation studies and personal observations, is given in Table D-I. This rating is in general agreement with sensitivity lists published previously.[14, 16] The categories used are subjective and arbitrary. Some investigators may prefer to include more species in the sensitive category while others may prefer to restrict the number. Also within any group, the degree of sensitivity will depend largely on the many environmental variables.

Only a few plant species are highly sensitive to fluoride

and injury is usually limited to plants in the sensitive group; injury has been observed on most of these species when leaf analysis revealed a fluoride content less than 50 ppm. Injury to plants in the intermediate group is infrequent. Injury to species in the resistant category is still more infrequent and has been observed only when fluoride concentrations in the foliage exceeded several hundred ppm. Only the more common species which fall into this category are listed.

Symptomatology

Leaves

Fluoride air pollutants enter the plant primarily through the leaves. Most of it apparently enters through the stomata, passes into the intercellular spaces and is absorbed by the mesophyll.[14] From the mesophyll the fluoride may move to other cells by simple diffusion or through the vascular tissue. It moves with the transpiration stream toward the leaf tips and margins where it accumulates in concentrations at least several times higher than the average concentration in the leaf as a whole.[16]

The characteristic symptom of fluoride injury on many broad-leaved plant species is necrosis, which occurs predominantly at the leaf tips and margins where the fluoride has accumulated. A dull, gray-green, water-soaked discoloration of tissues along the leaf tip and margin is the first sign of injury to appear on such sensitive species as apricot and European grape (Figures D-1 and D-2). This symptom may appear within 24 hrs of a fumigation with fluoride concentrations of several ppb or, more typically, after several days or weeks, if concentrations are lower. These "water soaked" tissues generally turn light to dark brown within 48 hrs of fumigation during hot weather. Lower temperatures tend to delay symptom expression as much as several days. In the field, symptom expression may be delayed several weeks after the critical threshold of fluoride accumulation has been reached if temperatures remain cool and no further stress is imposed on the plant. If the atmospheric concentrations are extremely high fluoride may be absorbed by leaves at a much faster rate than it is translocated. Under these conditions, lethal concentrations apparently build up at various locations in the leaf tissue producing scattered intercostal lesions (Figure D-3). The scattered distribution of the lesions, and the more frequent presence of chlorotic areas, are the distinguishing characteristics of this type of exposure.

Apricot leaves exposed to low fluoride concentrations first develop semicircular lesions 1-3 cm in diameter along the leaf margin. A narrow, sharply-defined, reddish-brown band less than 1 mm wide typically separates the necrotic tissue from the adjacent healthy tissue. Microscopic examination has shown that this band often consists of an abscission layer formed by cell division. The necrotic tissue soon breaks loose along this band and drops off, so that unless subsequent markings develop, the only remaining sign of the injury may be the irregularity of the leaf margins. When fluoride concentrations are higher, or the period of exposure is prolonged, larger areas of tissue are affected and injury continues to develop. Generally fluctuations in atmospheric fluoride concentrations, or in environmental conditions that influence development of injury, cause the necrosis to appear in successive waves. A narrow, dark, reddish-brown band produced by deposition of resins and tannins in the peripheral cells delimits and characterizes the necrosis formed by successive fumigations and gives the necrotic lesions a wavy, zonate appearance. The necrotic tissue may ultimately form a continuous band around the leaf affecting up to 100% of the leaf or may be limited to trace amounts at the tip or along one edge.

Although the necrotic tissue readily separates and may drop out, the apricot leaf itself rarely abscises, even when the fluoride levels in the leaves exceed several hundred ppm and the leaf is severely marked. However, defoliation has

TABLE D-I

Sensitivity of selected plants to fluoride

Sensitive

Apricot, Chinese and Royal
  Prunus armeniaca, L.
Boxelder
  Acer negundo, L.
Blueberry
  Vaccinium, sp.
Corn, sweet
  Zea mays, L.
Fir, Douglas
  Pseudotsuga taxifolia, Brit.
Gladiolus
  Gladiolus, sp.

Grape, European
  Vitis vinifera, L.
Grape, Oregon
  Mahonia repens, Don.
Larch, western
  Larix occidentalis, Nutt.
Peach (fruit)
  Prunus persica, Sieb. & Zucc.
Pine, Eastern white, lodgepole,
  scotch, Mugho
  Pinus strobus, L.,
  Pinus contorta, Dougl.,

Pinus sylvestris, L.,
  Pinus mugho, Turra.
Pine, ponderosa
  Pinus ponderosa, Laws.
Plum, Bradshaw
  Prunus domestica, L.
Prune, Italian
  Prunus domestica, L.
Spruce, blue
  Picea pungens, Englm.
Tulip
  Tulipa gesneriana, L.

Intermediate

Apple, Delicious
  Malus sylvestris, Mill.
Apricot, Moorpark and Tilton
  Prunus armeniaca, L.
Arborvitae
  Thuja, sp.
Ash, green
  *Fraxinus pennsylvania var.
  lanceolata*, Borkh.
Aspen, quaking
  Populus tremuloides, Michx.
Aster
  Aster, sp.
Barley (young plants)
  Hordeum vulgare, L.
Cherry, Bing, Royal Ann
  Prunus avium, L.
Cherry, choke
  Prunus virginiana, L.
Chickweed
  Cerastium, sp.
Clover, yellow
  Melilotus officinalis, Lam.
Citrus (lemon, tangerine)
  Citrus, sp.
Geranium
  Geranium, sp.
Golden Rod
  Solidago, sp.

Grape, Concord
  Vitis labrusca, L.
Grapefruit (fruit)
  Citrus paradisi, Mact.
Grass, crab
  Digitaria sanguinalis, L. Scop.
Lambs-quarters
  Chenopodium album, L.
Lilac
  Syringa vulgaris, L.
Linden, European
  Tilia cordata, Mill.
Maple, hedge
  Acer campestre, L.
Maple, silver
  Acer saccharinum, L.
Mulberry, red
  Morus rubra, L.
Narcissus
  Narcissus, sp.
Nettle-leaf goosefoot
  Chenopodium, sp.
Orange
  Citrus sinensis, Osbeck
Peony
  Paeonia, sp.
Poplar, Lombardy and Carolina
  Populus nigra, L. and *Populus
  eugenei*, Simon-Louis)

Raspberry
  Rubus idaeus, L.
Rhododendron
  Rhododendron, sp.
Rose
  Rosa odorata, Sweet
Serviceberry
  Amelanchier alnifolia, Nutt
Sorghum
  Sorghum vulgare, Pers.
Spruce, white (young needles)
  Picea glauca, Moench, Voss.
Sumac, smooth
  Rhus glabra, L.
Sunflower
  Helianthus, sp.
Violet
  Viola, sp.
Walnut, black
  Juglans nigra, L.
Walnut, English
  Juglans regia, L.
Yew
  Taxus cuspidata, Sieb & Zucc.

Resistant

Ash, European Mt.
  Sorbus aucuparia, L.
Ash, Modesto
  Fraxinus velutina, Torr.
Asparagus
  Asparagus, sp.
Birch, cutleaf
  Betula pendula var. gracilis, Roth.
Bridalwreath
  Spiraea prunifolia, Sieb. & Zucc.
Burdock
  Arctium, sp.
Cherry, flowering
  Prunus serrata, L.
Cotton
  Gossypium hirsutum, L.
Current
  Ribes, sp.

Elderberry
  Sambucus, sp.
Elm, American
  Ulmus americana, L.
Juniper, (most species)
  Juniperus, sp.
Linden, American
  Tilia americana, L.
Pear
  Pyrus communis, L.
Pigweed
  Amaranthus retroflexus, L.
Planetree
  Platanus, sp.
Plum, flowering
  Prunus cerasifera, Enrh.
Pyracantha
  Pyracantha, sp.

Squash, summer
  Curcurbita pepo, L.
Strawberry
  Fragaria, sp.
Tomato
  Lycopersicon esculentum, Mill.
Treeofheaven
  Ailanthus altissima, L.
Virginia creeper
  Parthenocissus quinquefolia, Planch.
Willow, several species
  Salix, sp.
Wheat
  Triticum, sp.

D3

been reported on certain other stone fruits and citrus.[17,19]
  The necrotic lesions described for apricot are typical of
the injury produced on sensitive, broad-leaved plants. The
wavy color pattern of the necrosis is the most definitive
characteristic, but the amount of color contrast varies among

species as does the color of the necrotic tissue. Some species,
e.g. boxelder, show little tendency for the necrotic tissue to
break away from the normal tissue at its juncture, but it may
become shattered and broken off in irregular pieces by wind.
  The most sensitive leaves on fruit trees such as apricot

and prune are those on sucker shoots with their softer, rank growth. Axillary and terminal buds are highly resistant to fluoride and trees have been observed to retain their capacities to produce new shoots for 10 successive years.

Fluoride sometimes causes a distinctive injury symptom on lilac. A reddish-purple discoloration develops first along the leaf margins and progresses into a mottled reddish pattern between the veins. More severe injury results in both chlorosis and necrosis.

Fluoride injury symptoms on needles of pine and other conifers consist of necrosis which begins at the tip of the current year's needles and progresses toward the base (Figure D-4). Injured tissue first becomes chlorotic and then turns buff to reddish-brown, depending on the species. Occasionally, bands of tissue part of the way down the needle become necrotic. Needles are most sensitive when they are elongating and emerging from the "fascicle" in the spring, and become progressively more resistant as the season progresses. Needles formed during preceding years are highly resistant to fluoride and are rarely, if ever, injured by current fumigations.

Solberg et al.[20] conducted detailed histological studies of the effects of fluoride on pine needles and observed that the tissue collapsed only a few cells in advance of the necrotic areas. Epidermis, hypodermis and xylem tissues were most resistant and parenchyma most sensitive. Phloem cells were the first to be injured. Phloem and xylem parenchyma, together with transfusion parenchyma cells, enlarged greatly, becoming extended and distorted. The protoplast then became granulated, vacuolated, and finally collapsed. These characteristics were useful in distinguishing fluoride-induced needle necrosis from that caused by sulfur dioxide and other agents.

Fluoride may cause a chlorotic symptom expression as on leaves of citrus (Figures D-5 and D-6) poplar (Figure D-7) and sweet cherry. The chlorosis, or yellowing, extends inward from the leaf margins between the larger veins. In its early development, the chlorosis is light yellow-green in color and shades gradually into the normal dark green tissue along the midrib and larger veins. With continued exposure to fluoride, the chlorotic tissue may become completely yellow, and the demarcation between chlorotic and green tissue becomes sharply defined. Severe defoliation has also been reported to accompany this stage of leaf injury[6]. Some of the more severely injured tissue at the leaf margins may eventually become necrotic. Chlorosis has been observed to be most common on many other plants when fumigated with hydrogen fluoride in greenhouses and growth chambers. It does not appear to be common in the field, but occasionally is associated with leaf necrosis in plant species on which necrotic symptoms normally predominate.

Symptoms of fluoride injury on monocotyledonous plants are essentially similar to those on broad-leaved species. On gladiolus, necrosis develops primarily at the leaf tips, and reddish brown waves denoting successive fumigations are striking and definitive (Figure D-8). Similar "bands" are also characteristic of fluoride toxicity on False Solomonsseal (Smilacina, sp.) and other sensitive species (Figure D-9). The zonation is absent only when the necrosis is caused by a single fumigation. The necrosis frequently extends further down one side of the leaf than the other. Sensitive varieties or iris (Iris, sp.), narcissus, tulip, and related species develop similar injury symptoms. Necrosis on cereal crops such as barley is light in color and sometimes almost white. These species are more resistant to fluoride, and necrosis observed in the field is more frequently due to hot, dry winds or other environmental stress.

Fluoride injury symptoms on corn consist of a chlorotic mottle, or "flecking," concentrated toward the margins and tips of the leaves (Figure D-10)[21]. Small, irregularly-shaped,

chlorotic spots develop between the veins gradually merging into continuous chlorotic bands. When injury is more severe, most of the leaf may become chlorotic. The yellowish to straw-colored chlorotic areas tend to be confined between the larger veins and concentrated along the outer edge of the interveinal zone. Tissues along the outer side of the large veins normally remain green, but the chlorosis may bridge these veins as it intensifies. When the injury is severe, some of the chlorotic tissue may become necrotic, particularly along the margins and at the tips of the leaves.

Fluoride injury symptoms on sorghum are similar to those on corn, but in fumigation experiments some varieties have shown a tendency to develop dark, brownish-red spots at the leaf tips and margins. Spots, 0.5 cm or more in diameter, may become necrotic in the center or smaller spots may fuse together and become necrotic but the tissue in scattered small spots generally remains turgid.[21-22]

Flowers and Fruit

Flower petals are rarely injured in the field. The only reported observations of injury are cited by Thomas[14] who lists petunia (Petunia, sp.) petals as intermediate in sensitivity, and Spierings,[23] who reported that cyclamen (Cyclamen, sp.) flowers were more susceptible to hydrogen fluoride than the leaves. Injury consisted of marginal necrosis of the petals and sepals. Gladiolus flowers are resistant to fluoride despite the extreme sensitivity of the leaves and bracts. Sepals and petals remain unmarked even when 50% or more of the leaf area is necrotic and the bracts subtending the flowers are equally damaged. Apple, apricot, cherry, and peach petals are also tolerant.

Some fruits may be indirectly more sensitive to fluoride than the leaves. The best known example of fluoride injury to fruit is the soft suture disease of peach (Figure D-11). This syndrome may be better termed "suture red spot" since this denotes a specific type of soft suture associated with fluoride,[24] and is characterized by premature redding and ripening of a local, rather sharply-delimited area along one or both sides of the suture line toward the lower (stylar end) third of the fruit. The red area contrasts sharply against the pale yellow or yellow-green background color. In some instances, premature ripening and swelling cause a local enlargement of the affected area. More often the tissues along the suture ripen without undergoing excessive enlargement, and the affected portion is typically over-ripe, soft, and slightly sunken by the time the rest of the fruit is ripe. Premature reddening may appear 2 weeks to 1 month before harvest. The early, sharply-defined coloring, even on fruits in shaded parts of the tree, is especially striking before the normal ripening coloration begins. Another symptom is the separation of the flesh along the suture. This splitting beneath the skin may occur even when symptoms are extremely mild. Reddening of the affected flesh in a local region along the suture is another good diagnostic aid with yellow-fleshed varieties such as Hale and Elberta.

Fluoride-induced suture red spot may be influenced by calcium and boron nutrition, and it has been a problem in certain areas where atmospheric fluoride concentrations have been very low. Even where fluoride concentrations were too low to cause necrosis of peach leaves, up to 90% of the fruit was rendered unsaleable. Suture red spot is not correlated with high fluoride concentrations in the fruit since the critical period of sensitivity appears to be early in fruit development when the pit is hardening and calcium demands are greatest. At maturity, peaches, like most fruit, never contain more than a few ppm of fluoride.

Less striking but basically similar symptoms attributed to fluoride have been described and illustrated by Bolay and Bovay[25] to consist of a local necrosis of the stylar (i.e. basal) end of apricot, cherry and pear fruits. A round or irregular sunken, dark brown to black lesion developed at the stylar end of the fruit as it ripened. This symptom has been noted on apricot fruits in two Utah orchards under conditions of moisture stress and poor nutrition. Although the fluoride levels of leaves in these orchards exceeded 200 ppm, the relation of fluoride to symptom expression was not known. No symptoms appeared on pear fruits in the same orchards.

A similar condition known as "snub nose" or "shrivel tip," in which the stylar end, or tip, of the cherry fruit ripens and shrivels a few days prematurely, has been observed on the Orb variety. The disorder may be caused by high fluoride concentrations alone, but is aggravated by water stress; almost indistinguishable symptoms can be caused by water stress alone. A "black tip" condition of sour cherries and peaches is also attributed largely, if not wholly, to water stress.

Factors Affecting Sensitivity

Every factor in the environment which influences the plant's vigor appears also to influence its sensitivity to fluoride. Mineral nutrition has a marked effect on plant growth and might be expected to exert a corresponding influence on sensitivity. McCune et al.[26] found that despite a limited effect on fluoride accumulation, nutrient relations influenced the severity of necrosis on gladiolus. Fluoride-induced necrosis was less when the plants were grown with low levels of nitrogen or calcium. When potassium, phosphorus, or magnesium were deficient, tip-burn was more severe. Deficiencies of iron or manganese had no effect on necrosis. Pack[8] reported that fluoride injury to tomatoes was more severe when the plants were grown under conditions of low calcium. Relationships between nutrition and sensitivity have also been shown by Brennen et al.[27] and Applegate and Adams[15].

D 5 Water relations have an important influence on the severity of fluoride damage, although the response observed under field conditions does not appear to agree with the results of controlled, greenhouse experiments. Zimmerman and Hitchcock[16] found that turgid, succulent plants grown under optimum moisture and fertility conditions were most sensitive to fluoride; however, extensive field observations have consistently shown that plants grown under neglected, unfavorable, arid conditions are most severely injured by fluoride. Trees growing on gravelly areas in an orchard, or on a slope with southern exposure, are consistently most sensitive. One striking example was observed where apricot trees in a neglected orchard had over 10% leaf necrosis while the necrosis on irrigated, well-managed and pruned trees in adjacent orchards was less than 1%. In the field, neglected plants may have adequate moisture in the spring but be subjected to increased moisture stress as the season progresses. This increase in moisture stress may promote the development of necrosis and lead to more injury than when plants are grown under an initial and continuous moisture stress.

Symptoms Resembling Injury by Fluoride

Diagnosis of fluoride injury occasionally may be complicated by the presence of symptoms which look similar to those produced by fluoride but whose cause is completely unrelated to fluoride pollution. Accurate diagnosis depends on familiarity with the normal appearance of plants and knowledge of the relative fluoride sensitivity of a wide range of species. The observer must be familiar with symptoms caused by other agents as well as the symptoms of fluoride injury. The more he knows about the local disease and injury problems caused by fungi, viruses, bacteria, insects, mites, improper nutrition or culture, temperature and moisture stress, and other "normal" environmental stresses, the more accurate and valid will be his diagnosis and evaluation.

Fluoride analysis is often a useful aid to diagnosis. For such data to have greatest value though, the observer must have some knowledge of what constitutes "normal" background levels. In the absence of an atmospheric fluoride source, plants commonly accumulate 5-10 ppm fluoride in their leaves during the course of a growing season, and normal levels of 10-20 ppm are not unusual. A few species, however, included tea (Thea, sp.), camellia and gifblaar (Gifblaar, sp.), have a unique capacity of accumulating vast quantities of fluoride, and foliar concentrations may reach several hundred ppm in the absence of atmospheric pollution[14].

If the fluoride levels in an area being studied are "normal" fluoride can be ruled out as the injurious agent. Unfortunately, the reverse doesn't hold. The presence of higher fluoride concentrations in plant leaves does not prove that the fluoride is injurious, but such data may give some indication if the relative sensitivity of the plant is known. Similarly, partly because of the lack of data denoting the direction or source of exposure, and partly because of the multitude of environmental factors influencing sensitivity, atmospheric fluoride analysis provides only a general guide as to the possible presence or threat of fluoride injury.

Diagnosis of suspected fluoride injury to vegetation should begin by the location and careful examination of sensitive, indicator species in the area. The more closely the degree of injury is related to the fluoride sensitivity of various species, the more confidence can be placed in the diagnosis. If leaf markings are confined to resistant or tolerant species, some other causal agent should be sought.

Several environmental stresses cause injury symptoms strikingly similar to those characterizing fluoride injury. Fluoride injury on many plants is most closely mimicked by marginal leaf burning caused by moisture stress (Figure D-12). Such symptoms may be misleading to the untrained observer when they appear on such fluoride-sensitive, indicator plants as apricot (Figure D-13). Moisture stress causes marginal necrosis of many broad-leaved plant species, especially when cool spring weather has induced soft, rank growth which is especially predisposed to injury. Drought-induced necrosis can often be distinguished by a rather diffuse zone of chlorotic tissue separating necrotic and healthy tissues. Low-temperature injury, consisting of necrotic leaf margins may also resemble fluoride injury (Figure D-14).

Necrosis of conifer needles (Figure D-15) is caused by so many stresses, and is so non-specific, that the total syndrome must be relied upon for diagnosis. The relative fluoride sensitivity of the affected and associated species is also helpful. Necrosis caused by other pollutants, especially chloride and sulfur dioxide, may also resemble fluoride injury not only on conifers, but on such fluoride-sensitive broad-leaved species as European grape (Figure D-16). Again, the relative sensitivity of different-aged tissues and different species must be considered.

Symptoms of virus and genetic disorders such as prune leaf spot and grape leaf roll may at times resemble fluoride injury (Figure D-17); therefore several different plant species should be examined for symptoms whenever possible.

Pesticides, especially oil sprays, organic phosphates, and other acutely toxic chemicals can cause necrosis similar to that caused by fluoride (Figures D-18 and D-19).

Some nutrient deficiency symptoms bear a close resemblance to fluoride-induced chlorosis. The marginal and interveinal chlorosis that characterizes manganese deficiency on plants such as peach, cherry, and citrus (Figure D-20) is so similar to mild fluoride toxicity symptoms that one must rely heavily on the appearance of symptoms on associated species. Zinc deficiency symptoms on leaves may also be confused with fluoride injury unless the total syndrome is evaluated and fruits can be inspected. The malformed fruit, leaf distortions, and rosetting associated with zinc deficiency are not associated with fluoride injury.

Symptoms of fluoride toxicity on corn are often similar to those produced by zinc or potassium deficiency, mite injury, genetic variation, or normal senescence. Generally the genetic mottle is brighter yellow in color. Similarity of fluoride injury to normal senescence renders diagnosis late in the growing season tenuous.

Several pathogenic agents can cause local, premature reddening and ripening of the suture of peach fruit, and the general name soft suture has been given to this expression regardless of cause. In all cases the affected area colors and ripens 2 or 3 days early.

A physiological type of soft suture characterized mostly by stress-related, early ripening of one side of the fruit was described and named soft suture by M. H. Dorsey in Illinois in 1944.[29] In contrast to the fluoride-induced soft suture, which is usually more prevalent on trees with a light crop, the condition was associated with overloaded, weak trees.

Growth-regulating chemicals such as the phenoxyacetic acids can also cause a soft suture expression when applied in excessive amounts to improve fruit size or to control weeds in orchards while the fruits are developing (Figure D-21). In contrast to fluoride-induced injury, symptoms are most pronounced near the stem end of the fruit and the swelling is more pronounced.

References

1. Haselhoff, E., Bredemann, G., and Haseloff, W., *Entstehung und Beurteilung von Rauchschäden,* Verlogsbuchhandlung Gebulder Berntreger, Berlin (1932).
2. MacIntire, W. H., "Soil content of fluorine and its determination", *Soil Sci.,* **29,** 105-109 (1945).
3. McCune, D. C., Hitchcock, A. F., Jacobson, J. S., and Weinstein, L. H., "Fluoride accumulation and growth of plants exposed to particulate cryolite in the atmosphere", *Contrib. Boyce Thompson Inst.,* **23,** 1-12 (1965).
4. Pack, M. R., Hill, A. C., Thomas, M. D., and Transtrum, L. G., "Determination of gaseous and particulate inorganic fluorides in the atmosphere", in Air Pollution Control, *Am. Soc. Testing Mater. Spec. Tech. Publ.,* **281,** 27-44 (1959).
5. MacIntire, W. H., Winterberg, S. H., Thompson, J. G., and Hatcher, B. L., "Fluoride content of plants", *Ind. Eng. Chem.,* **34,** 1469-1479 (1942).
6. Brewer, R. F., Sutherland, F. H., Guillemet, F. B., and Creveling, R. K., "Some effects of hydrogen fluoride gas on bearing navel orange trees", *Proc. Am. Soc. Hort. Sci.,* **76,** 208-214 (1960).
7. Leonard, C. D. and Graves, H. B. "Effects of air-borne fluoride on Valencia orange yields", *Proc. Florida State Hort. Soc.,* **79,** 79-86 (1966).
8. Pack, M. R., "Response of tomato fruiting to hydrogen fluoride as influenced by calcium nutrition", *J. Air Pollution Control Assoc.,* **16,** 541-544 (1966).
9. Stocks, D. L., "The effects of fluoride on the growth and reproduction of bush bean plants, *Phaseolus vulgaris L."*, *M. S. Thesis,* 48 pp., University of Utah (1960).
10. Treshow, M. and Harner, F. M., "Growth responses of bean and alfalfa to sub-lethal fluoride concentrations", *Can. J. Bot.,* **46,** 1207-1210 (1968).
11. Adams, D. F. and Sulzback, C. W., "Nitrogen deficiency and fluoride susceptibility of bean seedlings", *Science,* **133,** 1425-1426 (1961).
12. Treshow, M., Anderson, F. K., and Harner, F. M., "Responses of Douglas fir to elevated atmospheric fluoride", *Forest Sci.,* **13,** 114-120 (1967).
13. Mohamed, A. H., "Cytogenetic effects of hydrogen fluoride treatment in tomato plants", *J. Air Pollution Control Assoc.,* **18,** 395 (1968).
14. Thomas, M. D. and Hendricks, R. H., "Effects of air pollution on plants", in *Air Pollution Handbook,* ed. Magil, P.L., et. al., section 9, McGraw-Hill, New York (1956).
15. Adams, D. F., Applegate, H. G., and Hendrix, J. W., "Relationship among exposure periods, foliar burn, and fluorine content of plants exposed to hydrogen fluoride", *J. Agr. Food Chem.,* **5,** 108-116 (1957).
16. Zimmerman, P. W. and Hitchcock, A. E., "Susceptibility of plants to hydrofluoric acid and sulfur dioxide gases", *Contrib. Boyce Thompson Inst.,* **18,** 263-279 (1956).
17. DeOng, E. R., "Injury to apricot by fluorine deposit," *Phytopathology,* **36,** 469-471 (1946).
18. Miller, V. L., "The effect of atmospheric fluoride on Washington agriculture", in *Air Pollution,* ed. McCabe, L. C., chapter II, McGraw-Hill, New York (1952).
19. Brewer, R. F., "Some effects of hydrogen fluoride gas on seven citrus varieties," *Proc. Am. Soc. Hort. Sci.,* **75,** 236-243 (1960).
20. Solberg, R. A., Adams, D. F., and Ferchau, H. A., "Some effects of hydrogen fluoride on the internal structure of Pinus ponderosa needles," *Proc. 3rd Natl. Air Poll. Symp.,* 164-176, Pasadena, Calif. (1955).
21. Hitchcock, A. E., Zimmerman, P. W., and Coe, R. R., "The effect of fluorides on milo maize (*Sorghum sp.*)," *Contrib. Boyce Thompson Inst.,* **22,** 175-206 (1963).
22. Zimmerman, P. W., "Impurities in the air and their influence on plant life," *Proc. 1st Natl. Air Pollution Symp.,* 135-141, Stanford Res. Inst., Los Angeles (1949).
23. Spierings, F. H. G., "Effects of air pollution on crop yield," *1st Intern. Congress Plant Pathology,* London (1968).
24. Richards, B. L., "Similarities between disease symptoms, insect damage and chemical injury to plants," in *Evaluation of air pollution effects on plants,* R. A. Taft Sanitary Engineering Center HEW., Training Course (1957).
25. Bolay, A. and Bovay, E., "Observations sur les degats provoques par les composes fluorides en valais," *Agr. Romande,* **4A**(6), 43-46 (1965).
26. McCune, D. C., Hitchcock, A. E., and Weinstein, L. H., "Effects of mineral nutrition on the growth and sensitivity of gladiolus to hydrogen fluoride", *Contrib. Boyce Thompson Inst.,* **23,** 295-300 (1966).
27. Brennan, E. G., Leone, I. A., and Daines, R. H., "Fluoride toxicity in tomato as modified by alterations in the nitrogen, calcium and phosphorus nitrition of the plant", *Plant Physiol.,* **25,** 736-747 (1950).
28. Applegate, H. G. and Adams, D. F., "Nutritional and water effect on fluoride uptake and respiration of bean seedlings," *Iyton,* **14,** 111-120 (1960).
29. Dorsey, M. H. and McMunn, R. L., "Tree-conditioning the peach crop", *Univ. Ill. Expt. Sta. Bull.,* **507,** (1944).

D 6

Figure D-1. Characteristic type of necrosis caused by fluoride toxicity to apricot (*Prunus Armeniaca*, L.) under field conditions. The zonate reddish-brown margin by the green tissue, and the readiness with which the dead tissue breaks off are particularly symptomatic of exposure to fluoride.

D7

Figure D-2. Fluoride-induced necrosis on grape (*Vitis*, sp.) leaves. Typically, necrosis does not extend uniformly toward the center of the leaf but is most pronounced along local areas of the margin.

Figure D-3. Marginal and intercostal necrotic lesions on Italian prune (*Prunus domestica,* L.) characterizing injury caused by high fluoride concentrations. (Photo courtesy of Boyce Thompson Institute.)

D 8

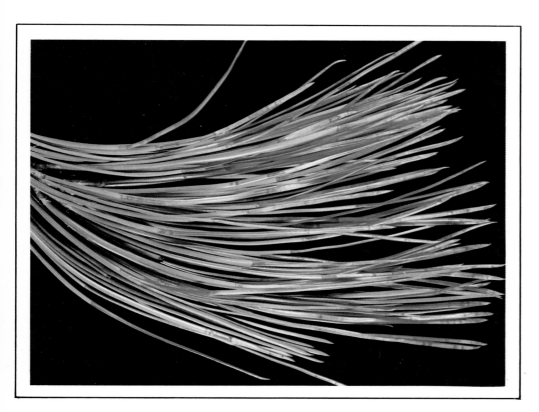

Figure D-4. Needle tip necrosis characterizing fluoride toxicity to conifers, specifically ponderosa pine (*Pinus ponderosa,* Laws), one of the most sensitive species. The prominant reddish-brown band delineating necrotic and green tissue is particularly diagnostic although many pathogens produce essentially similar symptoms.

Figure D-5. Chlorosis which represents the principal fluoride toxicity symptoms on a few species. Chlorosis may appear alone, as on these grapefruit (*Citrus,* sp.) leaves (see Figure D-6 also), or be followed by necrosis which begins at the margin and progresses inward. (Photo courtesy of C. D. Leonard.)

D 9

Figure D-6. Chlorosis on grapefruit (*Citrus,* sp.) leaf. (Photo courtesy of R. F. Brewer.)

Figure D-7. Chlorosis present in combination with fluoride-induced necrosis on Carolina poplar (*Populus eugenei,* Simon-Louis).

Figure D-8. Banding or zoning appearing on Snow Princess gladiolus (*Gladiolus,* sp.).

Figure D-9. Banding or zoning appearing on False Solomons-Seal (*Smilacina*, sp.).

D11

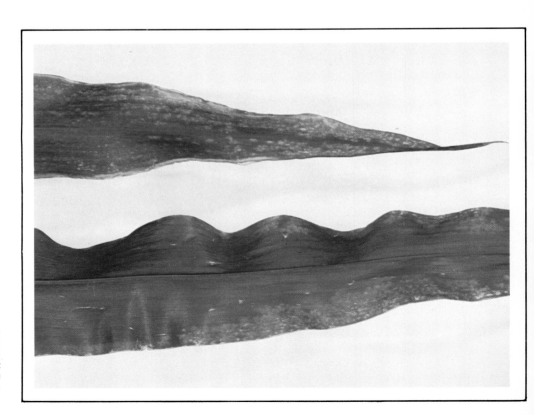

Figure D-10. Chlorotic flecking produced by fluoride on corn (*Zea mays*, L.). Yellowing and necrosis are typically most prominant along the leaf margin and toward the tip as shown.

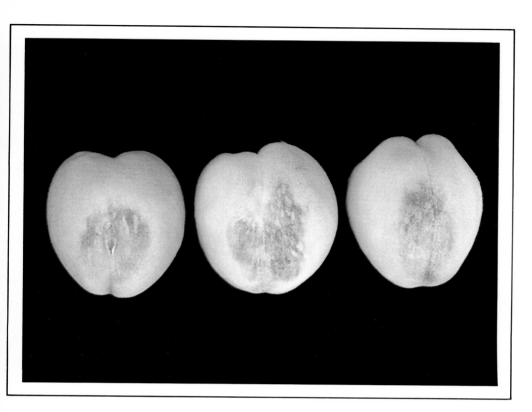

Figure D-11. Characteristic "soft suture" expression on peach (*Prunus persica*, Sieb & Zucc.) fruits which can be caused by fluoride toxicity or any one of several other pathogens. (Photo courtesy N. R. Benson.)

Figure D-12. Necrosis on quaking aspen (*Populus tremuloides*, Michx.) caused by moisture stress. Either high temperatures or lack of soil moisture can cause these symptoms. But In either case the zonations and reddish-brown band by the green tissues, which usually accompany fluoride toxicity, tend to be lacking.

Figure D-13. Necrosis on apricot (*Prunus Armeniaca,* L.) leaf. (See also Figure D-12.)

D13

Figure D-14. The type of low-temperature-induced necrosis which can mimic fluoride toxicity, not only on lilac (*Syringa vulgaris,* L.) as shown here, but on a number of species.

Figure D-15. Low-temperature injury on ponderosa pine (*Pinus ponderosa,* Laws). The symptoms alone so closely resemble fluoride toxicity that the total syndrome must be relied upon for diagnosis.

D 14

Figure D-16. Sodium sulfate injury on European grape (*Vitis vinifera,* L.) leaves. Necrosis tends to be more uniform around the margin, and less zonate, than where fluoride is involved.

Figure D-17. Necrosis and reddening caused by the leaf roll virus on European grape (*Vitis vinifera*, L.).

D 15

Figure D-18. Characteristic type of necrosis on sour cherry (*Prunus*, sp.) leaves caused by oil sprays.

Figure D-19. Necrosis caused by parathion insecticide spray on pole beans (*Phaseolus,* sp.) Similar markings can be caused by other pesticides on a number of species, but usually the markings are more randomly distributed over the leaf than when fluoride toxicity is involved.

Figure D-20. Manganese deficiency symptoms on citrus (*Citrus,* sp.). This interveinal chlorosis expression is virtually identical with that produced by fluoride where chlorosis expression is the main response. (Photo courtesy of C. D. Leonard.)

Figure D-21. Characteristic "soft suture" expression on peach (*Prunus persica*, Sieb. & Zucc.) caused by phenoxyacetic acid herbicides. Symptoms may be very similar to those caused by fluoride if only individual fruits are examined. Diagnosis should rely on the total syndrome. (Photo courtesy of N. R. Benson.)

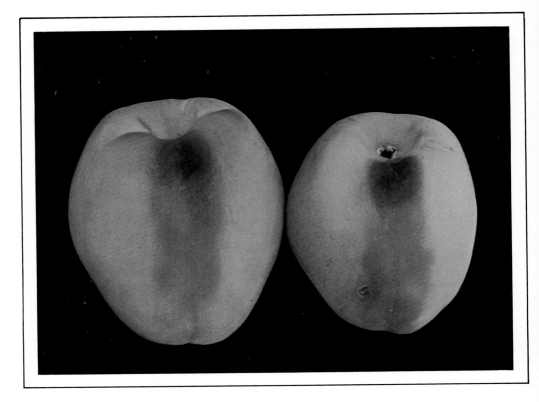

D17

Nitrogen Oxides and the Peroxyacyl Nitrates

O. Clifton Taylor
University of California, Riverside, California
and
David C. MacLean
Boyce Thompson Institute for Plant Research, Yonkers, New York

Introduction

Nitric oxide and nitrogen dioxide are the two more significant gases in the nitrogen oxide group of pollutants which are produced primarily by high-temperature combustion. The combined concentration of these two gases in large American cities ranges from 0.04—0.66 ppm[1]. On two occasions Los Angeles County recorded concentrations above 3 ppm but the concentration of nitrogen dioxide alone has rarely exceeded 1 ppm[2]. Within this order of magnitude, adverse effects from long-term exposure on photosynthesis and growth might be expected although significant foliar injury would probably not occur[3]. The major reason for the importance of nitrogen oxides as pollutants is their participation in photochemical reactions which produce ozone and the peroxyacyl nitrates (PANs), two highly phytotoxic oxidants.

The naturally occurring photochemical products of nitrogen oxides and reactive hydrocarbons were first identified as "compound-X" in 1956[4]. The C_2 member of the homologous series, peroxyacetyl nitrate (PAN), was first recognized in 1960[5]. The C_3 and C_4 homologues, peroxypropionyl nitrate (PPN) and peroxybutyryl nitrate (PBN), respectively, were also subsequently synthesized and used in plant studies. Both PAN and PPN were detected in polluted ambient air in 1963. Peroxybenzoyl nitrate (PBzN) was reported to be a much stronger eye irritant than either of the previously mentioned compounds[6] but it has not been used in plant studies. PAN is by far the most abundant of the series of compounds in polluted atmospheres and consequently has received the greatest attention as a phytotoxicant. Although PPN and PBN apparently occur in only trace amounts in heavily polluted atmospheres they may contribute significantly as phytotoxicants because they are several times more toxic than PAN.

Maximum concentrations of PAN measured in ambient air were reported to be 58 ppb at Riverside, Calif.[3], and 50 ppb at Salt Lake City[7]. Seasonal peak concentrations of PAN occur during the summer and fall months at Riverside, while relatively few peaks occur during the winter and spring months. This pattern is undoubtedly due to seasonal differences in the thermal inversion and direction of surface wind movement which in the summer and spring carries the polluted air mass into the Riverside area with a minimum of dilution and dispersion. The seasonal pattern for PAN concentrations does not correspond closely with patterns of NO_x observed in five California cities. In these cities highest levels of NO_x were reported in late fall and winter months[2].

Nitrogen Dioxide

In terms of direct effects on vegetation growing in the field the major sources of high levels of nitrogen dioxide are localized, accidental releases or spillage which cause relatively short periods of exposure. These high concentration exposures produce necrotic lesions and excessive defoliation[8].

Relative Susceptibility

The relative susceptibility of some plant species to NO_2-induced injury is presented in Table E-I. The species listed have been selected for study because of their economic importance in the area where the work was done or for the convenience of the investigator. It should be recognized that the categories of sensitivity used for tabulation in this table are relative and are based on subjective criteria. A plant species considered resistant by one investigator may be less tolerant of nitrogen dioxide than a species placed in the sensitive category by another.

The plant species listed in Table E-I are grouped into categories based on descriptions given by investigators for known nitrogen dioxide concentrations and durations of exposure, but the methods for evaluation of foliar injury used by the different researchers were not uniform. For example, Benedict and Breen[9] estimated sensitivity on the basis of the percentage of marked leaves on broadleaf plants and as a ratio of the length of marked area to total leaf length on grasses. A rating system which included percentage defoliation as well as necrosis was used by MacLean et al.[8,10]

Dosage response relationships with nitrogen dioxide are difficult to assess from published reports because of the lack of extensive experimentation and the wide ranges of plant species, toxicant concentration and exposure duration which were used. Concentrations of nitrogen dioxide which have

TABLE E-I

Sensitivity of selected plants to nitrogen dioxide[a]

Sensitive

Azalea *Rhododendron,* sp.	Hibiscus *Hibiscus rosasinensis*	Sunflower *Helianthus annuus,* L.
Bean, pinto *Phaseolus vulgaris,* L.	Lettuce (head) *Lactuca sativa,* L.	Tobacco *Nicotiana glutinosa,* L.
Brittlewood *Melaleuca leucadendra*	Mustard *Brassica,* sp., L.	

Intermediate

Cheeseweed *Malva parviflora,* L.	Dandelion *Taraxacum officinal,* Weber	Orange *Citrus sinensis,* Osbeck
Chickweed *Stellaria media,* Cyrill	Grass, annual blue *Poa annua,* L.	Rye *Secale cereale,* L.

Resistant

Asparagus *Asparagus officinalis,* L.	Grass, Kentucky blue *Poa pratensis,* L.	Nettle-leaf goosefoot *Chenopodium,* sp.
Bean, bush *Phaseolus vulgaris,* L.	Heath *Erica,* sp.	Pigweed *Chenopodium,* sp.
Carissa *Carissa carandas*	Ixora *Ixora,* sp.	
Croton *Codiaeum,* sp.	Lambs-quarters *Chenopodium album,* L.	

[a]Listing of plants obtained from references 8-13.

been used to date in fumigation experiments range from 0.18 ppm (for 10 days)[11], to 1000 ppm (for 1 hr)[12], and exposure times range from 0.2 hr (at 250 ppm)[8] to 22 days (at 0.2 ppm)[11]. With the exception of a few low-level, long-term exposures[11], most experimental fumigations were carried out at concentrations exceeding those normally encountered in polluted atmospheres.

Plant species vary widely in susceptibility to nitrogen dioxide and the threshold dosage required to produce injury on a specific plant may be affected significantly by the environmental conditions under which the plant was growing when exposed. Sensitive species such as pinto bean, tomato and cucumber may be injured by a 2-hr exposure to about 6 ppm nitrogen dioxide when they are growing under light intensity equivalent to full sunlight. Under extremely low light intensity equivalent to a very cloudy day these same plants may be injured when exposed for 2 hrs to 2.5-3.0 ppm. Other species are extremely resistant to nitrogen dioxide; Czech and Nothdurft[12] reported that both leaves and flowers of heath (*Erica,* sp.) were unaffected by exposure to 1000 ppm for 1 hr.

Although the nitrogen dioxide concentration and duration of exposure are both important factors to consider in determining the expected severity of injury to plants in the case of high-concentration exposures, there is no direct relationship between time and concentration, except within very narrow ranges. The concentration of nitrogen dioxide influences the extent of injury more than the duration of exposure[8].

Symptomatology

Low-concentration, long-term exposures to nitrogen dioxide do not induce typical acute foliar lesions associated with high-concentration, short-term exposures but subtle, although significant, effects have been observed. Continuous exposure of pinto bean and tomato plants for 10-22 days at less than 0.5 ppm suppressed growth without attendant foliar necrosis. The fresh and dry weight of the plants were reduced by as much as 25%. Thus, growth suppression may occur without concomitant foliar lesions at concentrations

frequently encountered in polluted atmospheres. Further research is necessary to ascertain the threshold levels for NO$_2$-induced chronic plant responses that occur after long term, low concentration exposures.

Acute foliar markings produced by high-concentration nitrogen dioxide exposures are characterized by water-soaked lesions, which first appear on the upper leaf surface (Figure E-1), followed by rapid tissue collapse[8] (Figures E-2 and E-3). These lesions, with time, extend through the leaf and produce small irregular necrotic patches[8,9,11] (Figures E-4 and E-5). Necrotic areas (Figures E-3 and E-6) are usually white to tan or brown and closely resemble SO$_2$-induced symptoms[9,13]. Necrosis on azalea injured by nitrogen dioxide is bronze colored[8]. Lesions occur between the veins of all sensitive plants and may be located anywhere on the leaf surface, but they are most prominent at the apex (Figure E-7) and along the margins[9,11]. In pigweed, cheeseweed, Kentucky bluegrass and mustard, nitrogen dioxide exposure results in a polished, dark waxy coating on the leaf surfaces that persists for about 1 week after exposure[9]. Leaves of sugar beets develop a grey glazed appearance[12]. In addition to foliar markings, high concentrations of nitrogen dioxide cause abscission of leaves and fruit of citrus (*Citrus,* sp.) (Figure E-8) and defoliation of azalea and hibiscus (*Hibiscus,* sp.).[8]

Factors Affecting Sensitivity

The extent, severity, and type of foliar lesions caused by a given nitrogen dioxide exposure can be affected by both internal and external factors. Genetic effects are obvious when the differences in sensitivity between species (Table E-I) or between varieties, cultivars, or clones of the same species are compared. For example, NO$_2$-induced effects in five orange varieties were qualitatively similar, but quantitatively the severity of the response differed sufficiently to rank the varieties in relation to their sensitivity to nitrogen dioxide[8]. Age of leaves also affects response to nitrogen dioxide. Older leaves were most sensitive in *N. glutinosa*[11], *Ixora*[8], and mustard[9]. In dandelion, cheeseweed, Kentucky bluegrass, chickweed, lambs-quarters and pigweed middle-aged leaves were most sensitive, whereas the sensitivity of middle-aged and old leaves was about equal in sunflower, annual bluegrass, and nettle-leaf goosefoot[9]. Necrosis was most severe on young leaves of citrus (*Citrus,* sp.) trees exposed to nitrogen dioxide[8].

External factors reported to affect plant sensitivity to nitrogen dioxide include soil moisture, light, and relative humidity, but information in these areas is limited. The few experiments conducted to study the effects of external factors have revealed that susceptibility was reduced by soil moisture stress[9], full sunlight, and low relative humidity[12].

Symptoms Resembling Injury by Nitrogen Dioxide

Accurate identification of NO_2-induced plant effect under field conditions is difficult. Necrosis produced by magnesium deficiency on old leaves is very similar to acute NO_2-induced necrosis. Other pollutants, including sulfur dioxide, chlorine and hydrogen chloride, and under some conditions ozone, produce necrosis that is indistinguishable from that produced by nitrogen dioxide. Symptoms such as those observed in experimental low-concentration nitrogen dioxide fumigations would not provide sufficient information to verify nitrogen dioxide pollution. Alterations in the balance of mineral nutrients can affect the chlorophyll content of plants; water stress can mimic the observed downward curvature of leaves; and a myriad of environmental and cultural factors can result in growth suppression.

Nitric Oxide

Oxidation of nitric oxide to produce nitrogen dioxide was used by Benedict and Breen[9] and the effects reported were considered to be attributable to nitrogen dioxide. No report of visible symptoms of leaf injury from nitric oxide have come to the attention of the authors and controlled fumigations conducted at Riverside failed to produce foliage injury if nitrogen dioxide was excluded from the system. The rate of carbon dioxide absorption (apparent photosynthesis) was suppressed during the exposure of pinto bean and tomato plants to concentrations of nitric oxide between 4 and 10 ppm but the normal rate was reestablished almost immediately after nitric oxide was removed. On the basis of these results, growth suppression may be expected without detectable leaf symptoms.

Peroxyacetyl Nitrate (PAN)

Man's activities at any particular time of day may produce significant diurnal variation in air quality but environmental conditions also have a pronounced effect on diurnal variations in PAN concentration. Photochemical reactions responsible for the production of PAN are dependent upon light intensity. The concentration of reactants increases under strong inversion conditions and when the surface wind movement is low. Elevated PAN concentrations move into an area with the polluted air mass when wind direction and/or wind velocity changes. Frequently, elevated concentrations of total oxidant move into Riverside, California, in late afternoon from the greater metropolitan Los Angeles area, reaching a peak briefly between 4:00 and 6:00 p.m.; then the level declines rapidly as darkness approaches. The total oxidant concentration usually reaches a peak before that of PAN and declines rapidly to near zero following sunset. Levels of PAN decline at night but concentrations in excess of 20 ppb often persist until the following day. On days in which elevated PAN concentrations occur only late in the afternoon and during the night even the most susceptible plants may escape injury, while significantly lower concentrations at midday may produce severe injury. Plants are much more sensitive to PAN if they receive full sunlight for 2 or 3 hrs before and after exposure to the toxicant[14].

Relative Susceptibility

In general, Noble's[15] listing of plants according to sensitivity to smog compares favorably with a listing of sensitivity to synthesized PAN. A few differences may be noted but these may indicate differences in methods of estimating injury or differences in environmental conditions which affect sensitivity.

Young rapidly-growing plants are more sensitive to PAN than older plants of the same species even though leaf tissue on some leaves of both plants is in the same stage of development. Young tomato or petunia plants with only three or four true leaves are more sensitive than comparable plants with six or eight leaves.

Peroxypropionyl nitrate (PPN) is several times more toxic than PAN and peroxybutyrl nitrate (PBN) is more toxic than PPN[14], but there is no distinguishing difference in injury symptoms produced by the three compounds. Fortunately PAN, the least toxic, is much more prevalent in polluted atmospheres than the other two homologues. Only trace amounts of PPN and PBN have been detected and they seldom reach measurable levels.

Susceptibility to PAN varies widely between species and often between varieties and strains. White- and purple-flowered petunias are more sensitive than the various shades of red, and romaine lettuce is much more sensitive than other types of lettuce. Some of the most sensitive plants such as petunia, tomato, dwarf meadow-grass and romaine lettuce may be severely injured by a 4-hr exposure to 15-20 ppb of PAN in the polluted atmosphere. Other resistant plants such as corn, onion, begonia and cotton are usually not injured with 75-100 ppb in a 2-hr exposure. A list of the sensitivities of some plants is shown in Table E-II.

Symptomatology

Middleton *et al.*[16] first described smog symptoms, now recognized as PAN-type injury, on spinach, garden beets, romaine lettuce and Swiss chard. He reported that in leaves the protoplasts of the mesophyll layer of cells, especially in the region of the stomata, collapsed and large air pockets took their place. These air spaces were apparently responsible for the glazed or bleached leaf symptoms. Leaves of sensitive species first develop a slightly oily or waxy appearance about 2 to 3 hrs after exposure to a toxic dosage of the PANs and the glazed symptom (Figure E-9) develops gradually. Bronzing (Figures E-10 and E-11) is an advanced stage which follows the glazing and usually develops fully after 2 or 3 days. Symptoms of PAN injury normally develop slowly following exposure to the toxicant and may require 24 to 72 hrs for full development.

Typically, PAN injury develops on only three or possibly four rapidly expanding leaves of sensitive species of plants. Very young leaves and the most mature ones are highly resistant (Figure E-12 and E-13). PAN injury appears only at the apex of the youngest susceptible leaf, as a diffuse transverse band across the intermediate-aged leaf, and at the base of the oldest susceptible leaf[3,17,18] (Figures E-14, E-15 and E-16). The two primary leaves of bean plants are notable exceptions because the entire abaxial surface of these leaves may be uniformly sensitive (Figure E-2).

A banding type symptom associated with smog was first described by Noble[19] in 1955. The bands were observed to occur in the same location on leaves of the same age; the location appeared to be related to cellular maturity (Figures E-9 and E-16). A distinct pattern of banding was observed in some form on all but one of fifty species examined after a single exposure to smog. Banding, along with glazing, bronzing, silvering and specific types of tissue collapse, were subsequently associated with injury produced by the PANs[18,20].

TABLE E-II

Sensitivity of selected plants to peroxyacetyl nitrate (PAN)

Sensitive

Bean, pinto *Phaseolus vulgaris*, L.	Grass, annual blue *Poa annua*, Linn.	Oat *Avena sativa*, L.
Chard, Swiss *Beta chilensis*, Hort.	Lettuce *Lactuca sativa*, L.	Petunia *Petunia hybrida*, Vilm.
Chickweed *Stellaria media*, Cyrill	Mustard *Brassica juncea*, Coss.	Tomato *Lycopersicon esculentum*, Mill.
Dahlia *Dahlia*, sp.	Nettle, little-leaf *Urtica ureans*, L.	

Intermediate

Alfalfa *Medicago sativa*, L.	Carrot *Daucus carota*, L.	Soybean *Glycine max*, Merr.
Barley *Hordeum vulgare*, L.	Cheeseweed *Malva parviflora*, L.	Spinach *Spinacea oleracea*, L.
Beet, sugar *Beta vulgaris*, L.	Dock, sour *Rumex crispus*, L.	Tobacco *Nicotiana tabacum*, L.
Beet, table *Beta vulgaris*, L.	Lambs-quarters *Chenopodium album*, L.	Wheat *Triticum sativum*, Lam.

Resistant

Azalea *Rhododendron*, sp.	Corn *Zea mays*, L.	Periwinkle *Vinca*, sp.
Bean, Lima *Phaseolus limensis*, L.	Cotton *Gossypium hirsutum*, L.	Radish *Raphanus sativus*, L.
Begonia *Begonia*, sp.	Cucumber *Cucumis sativus*, L.	Sorghum *Sorghum vulgare*, Pers.
Broccoli *Brassica oleracea*, L.	Onion *Allium cepa*, L.	Touch-me-not *Impatiens*, sp.
Chrysanthemum *Chrysanthemum*, sp.		

E4

Growth of tissue in the injured area is suppressed or inhibited and an indented or pinched region develops at the end of the transverse band as the remainder of the leaf tissue continues to expand (Figure E-13). Total collapse and necrosis of sensitive leaf tissue occurs when susceptible plants are exposed to high concentrations of PAN (Figures E-13 and E-17). Shortly after such high-concentration exposure, incipient chlorosis develops and the injured area gradually becomes flaccid or wilted. These are usually insidious changes and may be undetected except by an experienced observer. At least 24 hrs are required under a normal day-night regime for full development of the collapsed lesion. The collapsed tissue turns white to light brown or occasionally almost black on some species. Glazing and bronzing may develop along the edge of the collapsed band but are often absent when such severe injury occurs.

Although the glaze and bronze symptoms are usually confined to the lower or abaxial leaf surface, on some occasions this symptom may develop on the upper or adaxial surface (Figure E-18). This unusual expression has been observed most frequently on tobacco, petunia and tomato. The reason for this variation has not been explained.

Leaflets of compound leaves such as tomato and potato (*Solanum tuberosum*, L.) arise in basipetal succession, from the apex toward the base. The oldest tissue of the leaf is at the apex of the terminal leaflet. Consequently, when injured by a single exposure to PAN, symptoms appear at the apex of the terminal leaflet on the youngest susceptible leaf (Figure E-9). The next oldest leaf is usually injured near the base of the terminal leaflet and at the apex of the first two lateral leaflets. The third oldest susceptible leaf is subsequently injured at the base of the first two lateral leaflets and at the apex of the second pair of lateral leaflets while the more mature terminal leaflet remains uninjured. Extended exposure of plants for two or more successive days may produce separate and distinct bands of injury or the bands may overlap producing a broader pattern of injury. Noble[15] has reported observing four distinct bands of injury on leaves of *Poa annua* after 4 successive days of elevated smog levels. Leaf tissue continues to grow and mature at night when the leaves are not sensitive to PAN; therefore a band of non-injured tissue usually remains between the bands of injured tissue produced during the 2 consecutive days.

PAN injury on leaves of monocots develops as distinct transverse bands[15,20], from a few mm to perhaps 2 cm wide, across the leaf blade (Figure E-14). Glazing and bronzing seldom, if ever, appear but the band may be only chlorotic if injury is light or totally collapsed if injury is more severe. A single exposure for a few hours typically produces a band near the tip of a young leaf, near the middle of the next older leaf, and at the base of the next older leaf[15,20]. Apparently the vascular tissue of the monocot leaf is much more resistant than interveinal areas because the uninjured tip often remains green and healthy for several days or perhaps indefinitely while the injured band appears to be completely collapsed and the leaf folds downward at this point.

Growth suppression without detectable leaf injury has been detected when tomato and bean plants were exposed for several days to low concentrations of PAN. This inhibition of growth is assumed to be a result of suppression of photosynthetic activity[21], perhaps because of the disruption of plastids[22] and inhibition of certain enzyme activity[23].

Symptoms Resembling Injury by PAN

Reaction products of ozone and unsaturated hydrocarbons produce many of the glazing and bronzing symptoms used to characterize PAN injury. These products may add to the effects of ambient polluted air but because of their short half-life and the fact that they do not produce the complete syndrome of PAN or smog injury they are currently considered to be of minor importance, if in fact they do cause injury in the field. Under certain conditions, low concentrations of chlorine may produce lower-surface (abaxial) glazing and silvering resembling PAN injury. Chlorine, however, does not produce bands of injury and usually injures more mature tissue than PAN but in some instances it may be difficult to differentiate between the effects of the two toxicants. Cold injury sometimes produces a white collapsed band on leaves of grass and grains. This injury could be mistaken for PAN injury but usually close examination of cold injury reveals that the leaf is affected only where it bends or on the most exposed portion. A very light application of the herbicide diuron may produce chlorotic or bleached transverse bands on leaves of dwarf meadow grass and other grasses which resembles PAN injury.

References

1. Thomas, M. D., "The technical significance of air quality standards," *Environ. Sci. Technol.*, **3**, 628-638 (1969).
2. Tebbens, B. D., "Gaseous pollutants in the air," in *Air Pollution,* ed. Stern, I., vol. 1, Academic Press, New York (1968).
3. Taylor, O. C., "Effects of oxidant air pollutants," *Occupational Med.*, **10**, 53-60 (1968).
4. Stephens, E. R., Hanst, P. L., Doerr, R. C., and Scott, W. E., "Reactions of nitrogen dioxide and organic compounds in air," *Ind. Eng. Chem.*, **48**, 1498 (1956).
5. Stephens, E. R., Darley, E. F., Taylor, O. C., and Scott, W. E., "Photochemical reaction products in air pollution," *Proc. API*, **4**:III, 325-338 (1960).
6. Huess, J. M. and Glasson, W. A., "Hydrocarbon reactivity and eye irritation," *Res. Publ. GMK* **747**, General Motors Corp., Warren, Mich. (1968).
7. Tingey, D. T. and Hill, A. C., "The occurrence of photochemical phytotoxicants in the Salt Lake Valley," *Utah Acad. Proc.*, **44**:1, 387-395 (1967).
8. MacLean, D. C., McCune, D. C., Weinstein, L. H., Mandl, R. H., and Woodruff, G. N., "Effects of acute hydrogen fluoride and nitrogen dioxide exposures on citrus and ornamental plants of central Florida," *Environ. Sci. Tech.*, **2**, 444-449 (1968).
9. Benedict, H. M. and Breen, W. H., "The use of weeds as a means of evaluating vegetation damage caused by air pollution," *Proc. 3rd Natl. Air Pollution Symp.*, 117-190, Pasadena, Calif. (1955).
10. MacLean, D. C., Weinstein, L. H., McCune, D. C., Mandl, R. H., Hitchcock, A. E., and Woodruff, G. N., "Study to assess the impact of toxic propellants on KSC ecology," 80 pp., prepared for the *John F. Kennedy Space Center, National Aeronautics and Space Administration*, Cape Canaveral, Fla. (Dec. 1966).
11. Taylor, O. C. and Eaton, F. M., "Suppression of plant growth by nitrogen dioxide," *Plant Physiol.*, **41**, 132-135 (1966).
12. Czech, M. and Nothdurft, W., "Untersuchungen uber Schadigungen landwirtschaftlicher und gartnerischer Kulturpflangen durch Chlor-, Nitrose- und Schwefeldioxydgase," *Landwirtsch. Forsch.*, **4**, 1-76 (1952).
13. Middleton, J. T., Darley, E. F., and Brewer, R. F., "Damage to vegetation from polluted atmospheres," *J. Air Pollution Control Assoc.*, **8**, 9-15 (1958).
14. Taylor, O. C., "Importance of peroxyacetyl nitrate (PAN) as a phytotoxic air pollutant," *J. Air Pollution Control Assoc.*, **19**:5, 347-351 (1969).
15. Noble, W. M., "Smog damage to plants," *Lasca Leaves*, **15**:1, 1-24 (1965).
16. Middleton, J. T., Kendrick, J. B., and Schwalm, H. W., "Smog in the south coastal area of California," *Calif. Agr.*, **4**:11, 7-10 (1950).
17. Darley, E. F., Dugger, W. M., Mudd, J. B., Ordin, L., Taylor, O. C., and Stephens, E. R., "Plant damage by pollution derived from automobiles," *Arch Environ. Health*, **6**, 761-770 (1963).
18. Taylor, O. C., Stephens, E. R., Darley, E. F., and Cardiff, E. A., "Effect of air-borne oxidants on leaves of pinto bean and petunia," *Proc. Am. Soc. Hort. Sci.*, **75**, 435-444 (1960).
19. Noble, W. M., "The pattern of damage to vegetation by smog," *J. Agr. Food Chem.*, **3**, 330-332 (1955).
20. Juhren, M., Noble, W., and Went, F.W., "The standardization of *Poa annua* as an indicator of smog concentrations. I. Effects of temperature, photo period, and light intensity during growth of the test plants," *Plant Physiol.*, **32**:6, 576-586 (1957).
21. Dugger, W. M., Jr., Mudd, J. B., and Koukol, J., "Effect of PAN on certain photosynthetic reactions," *Arch. Environ. Health*, **10**, 195-200 (1965).
22. Thomson, W. W., Dugger, W. M., Jr., and Palmer, R. L., "Effects of peroxyacetyl nitrate on ultrastructure of chloroplasts," *Botan. Gaz.*, **126**:1, 66-72 (1965).
23. Mudd, J. B., "Enzyme inactivation by peroxyacetyl nitrate," *Arch. Biochem. Biophys.*, **102**:1, 59-65 (1963).

Figure E-1. Light green, water-soaked areas near the apex and margin of cucumber (*Cucumis sativus,* L.) leaf injured by nitrogen dioxide. Injury recorded 2 hrs after fumigation.

E6

Figure E-2. Brown necrotic lesions along margin and scattered in intercostal areas of muskmelon (*Cucumis melo,* L.) leaf injured with nitrogen dioxide. Injury recorded 48 hrs after fumigation.

Figure E-3. Intercostal collapse of leaf tissue on periwinkle (*Vinca,* sp.) injured by short-term, high-concentration nitrogen dioxide exposure.

E7

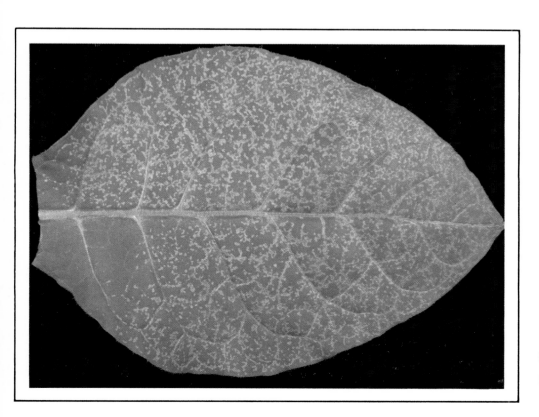

Figure E-4. Upper surface of tobacco (*Nicotiana,* sp.) leaf injured by nitrogen dioxide. Small, irregular necrotic lesions developed over entire surface but tended to concentrate along either side of small veinlets.

Figure E-5. Marginal and intercostal collapse of leaf tissue on romaine lettuce (*Lactuca sativa,* L.) plant injured by nitrogen dioxide.

Figure E-6. Nitrogen dioxide injury confined to intercostal area and along the midrib of tobacco (*Nicotiana,* sp.) leaves.

Figure E-7. Tip necrosis of very young leaves of carnation (*Dianthus caryophyllus*, L.) produced by nitrogen dioxide.

Figure E-8. Necrosis, intercostal collapse and leaf abscission on young tangelo *(Citrus,* sp.) exposed to high concentrations of nitrogen dioxide.

Figure E-9. Compound leaves of young tomato *(Lycopersicon esculentum*, Mill.) plants injured by PAN. Lower-surface glazing at the apex of the terminal leaflet of the youngest leaf and on tissue of similar stage of development on successively older leaves.

E10

Figure E-10. Primary leaves from pinto bean *(Phaseolus vulgaris*, L.) plants. Bronzing and glazing over entire lower surface of leaf injured by PAN. Non-injured leaf from plant grown in activated-charcoal-filtered atmosphere.

Figure E-11. Bronzing on lower surface of romaine lettuce *(Lactuca sativa,* L.) leaves fumigated with PAN.

E11

Figure E-12. Injury by PAN on leaves of Spanish peanut *(Arachis hypogaea,* L.). Chlorosis and brown necrosis was most prominent on upper surface of the leaf. Glazing, bronzing and silvering of lower surface did not develop.

Figure E-13. Collapsed and bleached lesions (diffuse transverse bands) on petunia *(Petunia,* sp.) leaves severely injured by PAN. Youngest leaf was injured only at the apex and oldest leaf developed only a trace of injury at the base.

E12

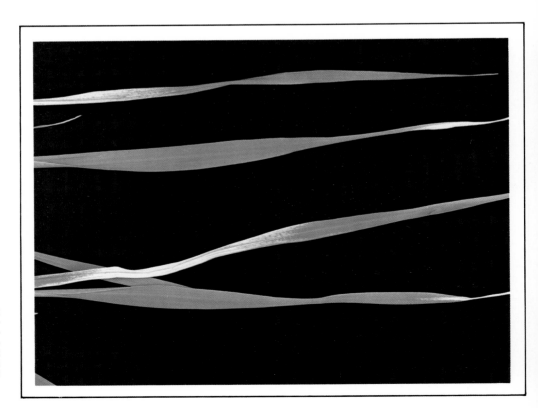

Figure E-14. Leaves of 3 week old oat *(Avena sativa)* plant injured by PAN. Bleached, necrotic, transverse band developed at tip of youngest injured leaf, about midsection of next oldest leaf and at the base of the third oldest leaf.

Figure E-15. Lower-surface glazing on tobacco *(Nicotiana,* sp.) leaves produced by PAN. Injury confined to apex of youngest leaf and to the base of the oldest leaf injured.

Figure E-16. Glazing, bronzing and collapse of petunia *(Petunia,* sp.) leaves produced by PAN. Youngest and oldest leaves are most resistant.

Figure E-17. Peroxyacetyl nitrate-type injury on romaine lettuce *(Lactuca sativa,* L.) and weeds exposed to smog in the field.

E14

Figure E-18. Peroxyacetyl nitrate injury on upper surface of expanding tobacco *(Nicotiana,* sp.) leaf. Glazing and bronzing occasionally occurs on upper surface but is normally confined to lower surface.

Other Phytotoxic Pollutants

Walter W. Heck
U. S. Department of Agriculture and National
Air Pollution Control Administration, Raleigh, North Carolina

Robert H. Daines
Rutgers University, New Brunswick, New Jersey

and

Ibrahim J. Hindawi
National Air Pollution Control Administration, Cincinnati, Ohio

F1

Introduction

Most of the pollutants considered in this chapter have not yet been studied extensively as agents responsible for phytopathological response. Some of these toxicants, since they enter the atmosphere from single source emissions (usually rather small in volume), have caused severe local problems, while the effects of others (primary products and little studied secondary products of combustion) may be more generally distributed[1-8].

Pollutants, in these categories, are listed in the general order of their importance as phytotoxic air pollutants: (1) unsaturated hydrocarbons (ethylene, acetylene, and propylene); (2) ambient oxidant complex excluding the three major components (ozone, PAN, and NO_x); (3) pesticides, especially the volatile herbicides; (4) chlorine; (5) ammonia; (6) hydrogen chloride; (7) mercury; (8) particulates, including the heavy metals and sulfuric acid mist; (9) hydrogen sulfide; and (10) carbon monoxide.

Limited studies have been carried out with these pollutants, and the laboratory information obtained has been considered in discussing and reviewing field injury. For each discussion of a specific pollutant or broad category of pollutant, a general review of background information, symptoms developed on vegetation by the pollutant, and relative susceptibilities of plant species are provided. The scope of the presentation is limited in some instances by the amount of research done on a particular pollutant and by its relative importance as a phytotoxic air pollutant.

Ethylene and Other Olefins

Ethylene, acetylene, and propylene are the important phytotoxic air pollutants in this group. Because responses of vegetation are similar for these three gases,[9, 10] discussion is limited primarily to ethylene. The ethylene concentrations required to produce injury to plants are between 100- and 1000-fold less than those for the other two olefins.

Olefins are by-products of any combustion process which involves organic compounds. Automotive exhausts produce large amounts of ethylene. Ethylene, as a by-product of polyethylene manufacture, has caused injury and economic loss of yield in cotton within a mile and a half radius of such an industrial plant.[11] As a contaminant of artificial illuminating gas, it has caused considerable injury when gas leaks have developed adjacent to greenhouse crops.[9, 12] As a by-product of metabolism of normal vegetation, ethylene plays a role in the senescence of mature tissues. Since so many sources are known which produce it, ethylene probably exists at some level within the atmosphere throughout the United States. As an air pollutant ethylene is thought to hasten normal aging of plant tissue and produce, under field conditions, an additive response to other pollutant effects.

Most work with ethylene has been conducted in laboratory or greenhouse-type fumigation experiments.[9, 13, 14] Very little field injury has been specifically associated with the ethylene problem other than that observed in commercial greenhouses.[15]

Relative Susceptibility

Plants studied in the laboratory showed some response to ethylene at concentrations as low as 1 ppm when exposed for 1 week or more. If plants are not killed or severely injured, recovery is usually rapid after the gas has been removed. The African marigold was found to be the most sensitive to ethylene; after a 24-hr exposure to 1 ppb it developed epinasty. Dry sepal in orchid was reported after a 6-hr exposure to 0.1 ppm and chlorosis and leaf drop, ranging from mild to severe, was observed in other sensitive species after a 30-hr exposure to 0.5 ppm. Table F-I lists a selected group of plants and their relative sensitivity to ethylene. Crocker[9] and Heck and Pires[14] have provided catalogs of plants studied thus far.

Symptomatology

Ethylene symptoms have been described from laboratory and greenhouse exposures.[9, 11-15] Ethylene acts as a growth hormone; it causes a general reduction in growth, stimulates lateral growth, and decreases apical dominance. Plant leaves or modified leaves may develop epinasty or show chlorosis, necrosis, or abscission. Bud abscission and failure of flowers to open properly have been reported for many floral crops (*i.e.*, sleepiness in roses and carnations). Ethylene appears to affect the older tissues first; however it also stimulates de-

TABLE F-I

Sensitivity of selected plants to ethylene[a]

Sensitive

Bean, Black Valentine
  Phaseolus vulgaris, L.
Carnation
  Dianthus caryophyllus, L.
Cotton
  Gossypium hirsutum, L.
Cowpea
  Vigna sinensis, Endl.
Cucumber
  Cucumis sativus, L.

Marigold, African
  Tagetes erecta, L.
Orchid
  Cattleya, sp.
Pea, cream
  Pisum sativum, L.
Peach
  Prunus persica, Sieb. & Zucc.
Philodendron
  Philodendron cordatum, Kunth.

Privet
  Ligustrum, sp.
Rose
  Rosa, sp.
Sweet potato
  Ipomoea batatas, Lam.
Tomato
  Lycopersicon esculentum, Mill.

Intermediate

Arborvitae
  Thuja orientalis, L.
Azalea
  Rhododendron, sp.
Carrot
  Daucus carota, L.

Gardenia
  Gardenia radicans, Thumb.
Holly, Japanese
  Ilex crenata, Thumb.

Soybean
  Glycine max, Merr.
Squash
  Cucurbita maxima, Duchesne

Resistant

Beet
  Beta vulgaris, L.
Cabbage
  Brassica oleracea, L.
Clover
  Trifolium, sp.

Endive
  Cichorium endivia, L.
Grass, rye
  Lolium multiflorum, Lam.
Oats
  Avena sativa, L.

Onion
  Allium cepa, L.
Radish
  Raphanus sativus, L.
Sorghum
  Sorghum vulgare, Pers.

[a]Listing of plants came from references 9, 12-14.

F2

TABLE F-II

Selected plants which are sensitive to oxidant[a,b]

Alfalfa[c]
  Medicago sativa, L.
Bean, pinto
  Phaseolus vulgaris, L.
Beet
  Beta vulgaris, L.
Clover[c]
  Trifolium, sp., L.

Endive
  Cichorium endivia, L.
Grapefruit[c]
  Citrus maxima, Merr.
Muskmelon[c]
  Cucumis Melo, L.
Oats
  Avena sativa, L.

Petunia
  Petunia hybrida, Vilm.
Pine, Eastern white
  Pinus strobus, L.
Spinach
  Spinacea oleracea, L.
Tobacco
  Nicotiana tabacum, L.

[a]Correlation of injury was made with a total oxidant meter. Injury could be caused by a number of pollutants; the symptoms have not been definitely associated with ozone, PAN or nitrogen dioxide.
[b]Listing of plants came from references 19, 22, and 24.
[c]Plants from Figures F-4 thru F-7.

velopment of new buds. Injury associated with ethylene usually develops slowly over a long period. This chronic type of injury may be mild or severe and may be associated with growth effects. Acute injury, in which symptoms develop rapidly and are severe, is not associated with this gas.

Necrosis of sepals on orchid flowers is a common effect of ethylene (Figure F-1). Epinasty of young rose leaves and interveinal chlorosis of older leaves are shown in Figure F-2.

Ambient Oxidant Complex

A potentially large group of compounds of an oxidant nature are believed to be present in polluted atmospheres. (The discussion of this group does not include ozone, PAN, and nitrogen dioxide, which are dealt with in other chapters.) Specific response of plants to irradiated auto exhaust, or to other irradiated and non-irradiated organic gas mixtures with ozone or nitrogen oxide, and to ambient oxidant pollutants suggests the existence of such an oxidant com-

plex although no specific compounds have been definitely identified. [16-24]

Symptoms associated with the oxidant complex are closely related to those caused by ozone and PAN. In certain laboratory tests the primary pollutants used (those present before atmospheric reactions) would have negated the presence of either ozone or PAN. In other cases, the age of plant tissue, or the pattern of injury on sensitive test plants, suggested a pollutant other than ozone or PAN. Field injury symptoms closely resemble those reported for ozone and PAN, but the pattern of response is sufficiently different that accurate diagnosis of PAN or ozone is not possible.

Relative Susceptibility

On several occasions irradiated mixtures of auto exhaust and nitrogen oxides, formaldehyde and nitrogen oxides, and ethylene and nitrogen oxides generated high concentrations of oxidant (0.4-0.7 ppm) but little or no injury was produced on sensitive vegetation.[16] This suggests that the oxidants generated in these reactions were not phytotoxic.

Specific oxidants, other than ozone, PAN and nitrogen dioxide have not been identified as toxicants in polluted atmospheres. Since a total oxidant index is composed of these three toxicants, as well as other compounds, it is impossible to discuss relative susceptibility in relationship to concentrations of any general or specific groups of pollutants. Laboratory exposures suggest the formation of extremely toxic pollutants at very low concentrations, perhaps in the ppb range.

Relative susceptibility of plants to oxidants, presumed to be other than PAN and ozone, produced by laboratory exposures to various gas mixtures is shown in Table F-11.

Symptomatology

Injury may be chronic or acute, the acute symptoms being more difficult to separate from symptoms caused by ozone-PAN combination.

In one study, plant symptoms were associated with four classes of phytotoxicants produced in irradiated auto exhaust.[22] Classes two and four were similar to PAN and ozone injury. Class one involved the palisade cells; injury developed near the tip of young leaves of tobacco or petunia, more toward the base of slightly older leaves, and at the base of the newly expanded leaves. The pattern was similar to that reported for PAN, but injury was noted first to palisade cells. Initially, a water-logged appearance developed on the upper surface of the leaf; later, injured tissue became reddish-brown and then developed a light or dark tan or bronze color in the necrotic areas. In severe cases a complete collapse of leaf tissue occurred. Class three injury developed on the upper surface of middle-aged leaves. The most characteristic symptom of this class developed on tobacco leaves, but injury was also noted on bean and petunia leaves. The injury was characterized by dehydrated and bleached lesions (fleck-like) on the upper leaf surfaces. In tobacco, this injury was first noted in those leaves that had just reached maturity (intermediate-aged leaves). It was similar to that caused by ozone, except that the lesions did not appear on the older leaves (Figure F-3). Class three injury was indistinguishable from that caused by ozone on bean leaves.

Plant injury, similar to that found on leafy vegetable crops in the Los Angeles Basin, was reproduced by treatment of plants with the reaction products of ozone and various olefins. This injury appeared as a glazing or bronzing on the under surface of spinach, endive and beet leaves, and as speckled necrosis on oats and alfalfa.[19]

Reaction products of mixtures of ozone with 1-pentene, 1-hexene, or 3-heptene caused PAN-type injury to 14-day old primary leaves of pinto bean, but not to 8-day old pinto bean or petunia leaves.[24] These reaction products, most toxic to recently matured leaves, caused an evenly distributed glazing and bronzing over the lower surface of the leaf. The injury often extended through the thickness of the leaf and appeared as necrotic spots on the upper surface.[18] Reaction products of irradiated mixtures of ozone-olefin caused injury to petunia and 8-day old bean leaves; this injury was similar to that caused by irradiated automobile exhaust, and by irradiated mixtures of nitrogen dioxide and olefins.[24]

Irradiation of formaldehyde or propionaldehyde produced high concentrations of oxidant. Products of formaldehyde irradiation caused no plant injury although products of propionaldehyde irradiation caused appreciable oxidant-type injury to tobacco, pinto beans, and petunia leaves.[16]

Figures F-4 thru F-7 show varied symptoms in field plants (muskmelon, alfalfa, clover, and grapefruit) associated with the oxidant complex, but not specifically related to ozone or PAN.

Herbicides

Herbicides form a ubiquitous group of chemicals which are becoming of increasing concern as potential air pollutants.

Selective weed killers have become widely used to control undesirable plants, since the herbicidal action of 2,4-dichlorophenoxyacetic acid (2,4-D) and 2,4,5-trichlorophenoxyacetic acid (2,4,5-T) was first reported in 1944 by Hammer and Tukey.[25] Although, these materials destroyed many weed species, economic loss occasionally resulted, especially in the 1940's and early 1950's, from volatile compounds or drift from spray or dusting operations. There have been occasional reports of severe plant injury caused by air-borne herbicides in the vicinity of industries that produce those chemicals.

Perhaps the most publicized and extensive case of herbicide injury to crop plants was that reported by Dunlap[26] along the Gulf coast area of Texas. Injury to about 10,000 acres of cotton was recorded at distances of 15-20 miles from a 2,4-D aerial dusting of rice (Oryza sativa, L.) fields. The extent of injury depended on the 2,4-D dose received and on the rate of plant growth at the time of exposure. In mild cases, only a few distorted leaves occurred near the top of the plant. In more severe responses all of the new growth was affected.

Sodium arsenite is often used in addition to weed control sprays to assist in harvesting operations. When these defoliating sprays are applied as a mist during windy conditions, trees, fruits, and vegetable crops may be injured.

Although herbicides have long been accepted as environmental pollutants which affect sensitive vegetation, the air-pollution aspects of volatile herbicides have not been widely explored. However, there is growing evidence that some 2,4-D compounds may be present in the ambient atmosphere in some parts of the eastern United States at levels sufficient to cause adverse growth effects on sensitive vegetation.

Relative Susceptibility

No precise relationships between air concentrations of pollutants and sensitivity of vegetation have been obtained at the present time. Some plants, which are apparently more sensitive to 2,4-D than others are listed in Table F-III. From field observations, grape and boxelder appear to be among the most sensitive since they respond to 2,4-D when other plants showed no evidence of injury. Injury to grape may result from exposure to levels in the ppb range.

Plant susceptibility to sub-lethal exposures of 2,4-D is markedly influenced by the growth condition of the plant and by environmental factors. Since most of the injury is expressed by growth response, the plant must be growing in order to show injury. In addition, plants in shaded areas respond more slowly than those exposed to direct sunlight. Because of these various factors which affect plant response to the 2,4-D type herbicide, differences in lists showing plant susceptibility should be expected.

Symptomatology

Reports of general herbicide injury, which have been reprinted in numerous publications will not be repeated here. Figures F-8 thru F-10 are included to depict injury from herbicide drift. However, since pictures associated with injury from herbicide concentrations found in ambient atmospheres are not usually available, general symptoms associated with low-level exposure to 2,4-D type herbicides are discussed.

Affected cotton leaves exhibit a yellow-green mottling or stippling and vein clearing may be pronounced. Tomato, poinsettia (Poinsettia, sp.) and, to a less extent, pepper plants may exhibit pronounced epinasty and twisting of plant

TABLE F-III

Sensitivity of selected plants to 2,4-dichlorophenoxyacetic acid[a]

Sensitive

Apple
Malus, sp.
Birch
Betula, sp.
Boxelder
Acer negundo, L.
Dogwood
Cornus, sp.
Elderberry
Sambucus, sp.
Forsythia
Forsythia, sp.
Grape
Vitis, sp.

Hickory
Carya, sp.
Lambs-quarters
Chenopodium album, L.
Linden
Tilia, sp.
London plane tree
Platanus acerifolia (Ait.) Willd.
Maple, Norway
Acer platanoides, L.
Oak, black
Quercus velutina, Lam.
Sorrell
Rumex, sp.

Sumac
Rhus, sp.
Tobacco
Nicotiana, sp.
Tomato
Lycopersicon esculentum, Mill.
Treeofheaven
Ailanthus altissima, Mill.
Wisteria
Wisteria, sp.
Yellow wood
Cladrastis lutea, Koch
Zinnia
Zinnia, sp.

Intermediate

Aster, wild
Aster, sp.
Cedar
Cherry
Prunus, sp.
Cherry, choke
Prunus virginiana, L.
Corn
Zea mays, L.
Gladiolus
Gladiolus, sp.
Hemlock
Tsuga, sp.

Mulberry
Morus, sp.
Oak, pin
Quercus palustris, L.
Oak, red
Quercus palustris, L.
Peach
Prunus persica, Sieb. & Zucc.
Potato
Solanum tuberosum, L.
Privet
Ligustrum, sp.

Ragweed, giant
Ambrosia trifida, L.
Rhododendron
Rhododendron, sp.
Rose
Rosa, sp.
Spruce, Colorado blue
Picea pungens, Englm.
Sweetgum
Liquidambar styraciflua, L.
Yew
Taxus, sp.

Resistant

Ash
Fraxinus, sp.
Bean, bush
Phaseolus vulgaris, L.
Cabbage
Brassica oleracea, L.

Eggplant
Solanum melongena, L.
Pear
Pyrus communis, L.
Peony
Paeonia, sp.

Rhubarb
Rheum rhaponticum, L.
Sorghum
Sorghum vulgare, Pers.

[a]Listing of plants came from references 26 and 27 and from personal observations of R. H. Daines.

parts.[27] These symptoms may take a pronounced form for only a relatively short period after exposure. In one case, tomato plant distortion was first observed by the grower at 7:30 a.m.; by noon the response was less pronounced; and by nightfall the epinasty and twisting had largely disappeared. On the following day injury to the epidermal cells on the lower surface of the tomato leaves was quite noticeable as a sunscald type of injury. It is not clear whether this injury resulted from the herbicide or from exposure of the undersurface of the twisted leaves in the direct sunlight.

Symptoms resembling "suture red spot" on peaches have been reported after application of herbicides. Affected fruits develop hypertrophy along the suture that shows more color; this part may soften ahead of the rest of the peach. This response is discussed in greater detail in the section on fluoride injury to vegetation.

Arsenic trioxide injury on sensitive fruit and vegetable crops produces necrotic spots on the leaves (Figure F-8), petioles, twigs, and fruits of affected plants. When peach trees are involved, heavy leaf fall accompanied by the killing of the smaller twigs may occur.

Mild to severe interveinal necrosis and chlorosis may occur on broad-leaved plants as a result of drift or residual soil applications of atrazine (Figure F-9). These symptoms may resemble those caused by other air pollutants.

Figure F-10 shows slight to severe growth malformations of sensitive leaves, resulting from application of 2,4-D type herbicides.

Chlorine

The occurrence of chlorine injury to vegetation is probably frequent, but is usually confined to localized areas. Chlorine as a phytotoxic pollutant has been associated primarily with: accidental release from storage tanks and underground lines carrying liquid chlorine; water purification plants and chlorination of swimming pools; industrial plants producing chlorine; accidental releases from chlorox manufacture; and, to some extent with refineries, glass making, and incineration of chlorine-containing plastics. Some reports of continuous release are associated with the refining of rare metals. Injury to vegetation was generally noted at distances less than a mile from the source except for accidental releases of large volumes of chlorine. Although laboratory fumigations have been reported,[1,4,7,28-33] the majority of reported injuries have been observed in the field.

Relative Susceptibility

Zimmerman[32] used concentrations of 0.46-2.95 ppm in fumigations that lasted 20-280 min. He reported that injury first appeared to the older leaves; stem tissue was also injured at the high concentrations of chlorine used in these studies.

TABLE F-IV
Sensitivity of selected plants to chlorine injury[a]

Sensitive

Alfalfa[b]
  Medicago sativa, L.
Apple, crab
  Malus baccata, Borkh.
Blackberry
  Rubus, sp.
Boxelder
  Acer negundo, L.
Buckwheat
  Fagopyrum esculentum, Moench.
Chestnut, horse
  Aesculus hippocastanum, L.
Chickweed
  Stellaria media, Cyrill.
Coleus
  Coleus, sp.
Corn[c]
  Zea mays, L.
Cosmos
  Cosmos, sp.
Gomphrena[c]
  Gomphrena, sp.

Grass, Johnson
  Holcus halepensis, L.
Johnny-jump-up
  Viola palmata, L.
Maple, sugar
  Acer saccharum, Marsh.
Mustard[c]
  Brassica, sp.
Oak, pin
  Quercus palustris, L.
Onion[c]
  Allium cepa, L.
Pine, white
  Pinus strobus, L.
Primrose
  Primula vulgaris, Huds.
Privet
  Ligustrum, sp.
Radish[d]
  Raphanus sativus, L.
Rose, tea
  Rosa odorata, sweet

Sassafras
  Sassafras albidum, Nutt, Nees.
Sunflower[c]
  Helianthus annuus
Sweetgum
  Liquidambar styraciflua, L.
Tobacco[c]
  Nicotiana tabacum, L.
Treeofheaven
  Ailanthus altissima, L.
Tulip
  Tulipa, sp.
Venus-looking-glass
  Specularia perfoliata (L.) A. DC.
Virginia creeper
  Parthenocissus quinquefolia, Planch.
Witch Hazel
  Hamamelis virginiana, L.
Zinnia[c]
  Zinnia, sp.

Intermediate

Azalea[e]
  Rhododendron, sp.
Bean[e], Scotia
Bean[e], pinto
  Phaseolus vulgaris, L.
Cheeseweed
  Malva rotundifolia, L.
Cherry, black
  Prunus serotina, Ehrhe.
Cowpea[e]
  Vigna sinensis, Endl.
Cucumber[d]
  Cucumis sativus, L.
Dahlia[d]
  Dahlia, sp.
Dandelion[d]
  Taraxacum officinale, Weber
Fern, braken
  Pteridium aquilinium, L.

Geranium[e]
  Geranium, sp.
Grape
  Vitis, sp.
Grass, annual blue
  Poa annua, L.
Gum, black
  Nyssa sylvatica, Marsh.
Halesia
  Halesia, sp.
Nasturtium[d]
  Tropaeolum, sp.
Nettle-leaf goosefoot
  Chenopodium murale, L.
Orange, mock
  Philadelphus, sp.
Peach
  Prunus persica, Sieb. & Zucc.
Petunia[e]
  Petunia hybrida, Vilm.

Pine, jack
  Pinus banksiana, Lamb.
Pine, loblolly
  Pinus taeda, L.
Pine, shortleaf
  Pinus echinata, Mill.
Pine, slash
  Pinus caribaea, Morelet
Rhodotypos
  Rhodotypus, sp.
Squash[e]
  Cucurbita moschata, Duchesne
Tobacco
  Nicotiana tabacum, L.
Tomato[d]
  Lycopersicum esculentum, Mill.
Wandering Jew
  Zebrina, sp.

Resistant

Begonia[f]
  Begonia rex, Putz.
Corn, field
  Zea mays, L.
Eggplant
  Solanum melongena, L.
Grass, Kentucky blue
  Poa pratensis, L.
Hemlock
  Tsuga, sp.
Holly, Chinese
  Ilex chinensis, Loes.

Lambs-quarters[f]
  Chenopodium album, L.
Oak, red
  Quercus, sp.
Olive, Russian
  Elaeagnus angustifolia, L.
Oxalis[f]
  Oxalis, sp.
Pepper[f]
  Capsicum, sp.

Pigweed
  Amaranthus retroflexus, L.
Polygonum[f]
  Polygonum, sp.
Soybean
  Glycine max, Merr.
Tobacco
  Nicotiana tabacum, L.
Yew
  Taxus, sp.

[a]Listing of plants came from references 1, 7, 28, 29, 32, and 35.
[b]Exposed at 0.10 ppm/2 hr.
[c]Exposed at 0.10-0.25 ppm/4 hr.
[d]Exposed at 0.50 ppm/4 hr.
[e]Exposed at 0.80 ppm/4 hr.
[f]Exposed at 1.0 ppm/4 hr.

F5

Benedict and Breen[1,2] exposed a group of common weeds to concentrations of 0.5-2.5 ppm chlorine for 4-hr periods. They found mustard, chickweed, and sunflower to be the most sensitive with Kentucky bluegrass, lambs-quarters, and pigweed most resistant. Injury was less severe under conditions of low soil moisture.

Brennan et al.[28] reported injury to alfalfa and radish foliage after a 2-hr exposure to 0.1 ppm of chlorine. They exposed twenty-six species to 0.10-1.0 ppm for periods of 2- or 4-hr exposures or both. They reported that drought increased plant resistance to chlorine exposures and that leaves being wet at the time of fumigation did not alter foliage sensitivity.

Slash, shortleaf and loblolly pines were equally resistant to chlorine-induced injury with the current season's needles being most sensitive.[29]

Leaves of sugar maple and crab apple trees, observed in a chlorine-polluted area, were brown and dropping, whereas field corn only a few feet away was unmarked. Injury to horse-chestnut (*Aesculus hippocastanum*, L.) was largely marginal but treeofheaven, Virginia creeper and blackberry exhibited intercostal markings. Certain varieties of tulip exhibit a bleach, especially to the under-surface of the older and middle-aged leaves, when other plants around them remain unaffected.

Reports indicate that levels of sensitivity are close to those for sulfur dioxide but plants may be more sensitive to chlorine.[1,7,28] Defoliation of plants has been reported with high-level, short-term field fumigations; the defoliation may occur with no acute markings on the leaves. Growth effects have not been reported for chlorine. Table F-IV lists plants in order of their relative sensitivity to chlorine.

Symptomatology

Injury associated with chlorine is primarily of an acute type but chronic symptoms, leaf abscission and epinasty have been reported. The injury pattern may be similar to those of sulfur dioxide, ozone, or other oxidants.

In 1932 Stout[31] described chlorine injury to lettuce (*Lactuca*, sp.), weeds, and grasses. Lettuce developed necrotic lesions along the margins of the outer leaves where injury was most severe. Injury often extended in solid areas towards the center and base of the leaf (Figure F-11); when concentrations were lower, brown spots occurred scattered over the leaf surface. At further distances from the source, the outer leaves of the lettuce plants exhibited superficial glossy gray or bronze discoloration to their under-surface. Injury to tall thick strands of grass and weeds appeared as pale yellowish-white bleached leaf tips.

Zimmerman[32] reported, in laboratory experiments, that injury first appeared as interveinal chlorosis in the older leaves followed by bleaching and breakdown of leaf tissue. Injury was often similar to that reported for sulfur dioxide.

Brennan et al.[28,34] found that symptoms of chlorine injury were variable. Necrosis and bleaching of leaves was most common. Marginal necrosis was pronounced in some species but was scattered in others, either between veins or along veins. Intercostal necrotic streaks were seen in corn. Onion leaves and pine needles showed a white or tan to brown tip necrosis.

Old and middle-aged leaves were readily injured by chlorine whereas the younger leaves were not injured (Figure F-11). Injury was found on both leaf surfaces but the upper surface appeared to be most sensitive (Figures F-12 and F-13). Several species developed orange-brown necrotic areas (Figure F-14). Johnson grass exhibited a silvery-whitish upper-surface injury after exposure to low concentrations of chlorine. Occasionally chlorotic injury may develop (Figure F-15). In certain plant species bleaching or flecking occurred which was indistiguishable from ozone injury (Figure F-13 and F-16). Abscission of injured leaves occurred only on a single species of *Chenopodium*.

Hill[35] has reported several types of symptoms for a variety of plants studied in the field. Epinasty on tomato was a common symptom. Upper-surface bleaching on sassafras and wild cherry and brown fleck-like lesions on witch hazel were common. Necrotic stipple on black gum and oak were occasionally found. Bifacial intercostal necrosis was observed on witch hazel and sassafras. Needle necrosis and chlorotic mottle were common on pine, especially white pine. Extensive needle drop was found in white pine and leaf drop was reported for mock orange (*Philadelphus* sp.), wild cherry, and witch hazel. Injury to corn was noted as interveinal necrotic streaks.

Zimmerman[32] recorded leaf drop in buckwheat and peach seedlings following exposure to chlorine. Schmidt[33] reported defoliation following chlorine fumigations of peach, apple, apricot and quince (*Cydonia*, sp.) trees. Leaf drop has been noted by the authors on both privet and wild cherry.

A variety of field symptoms showing chlorine injury are shown in Figures F-11 thru F-18.

Ammonia

Reports of field injury from gaseous ammonia have increased since anhydrous ammonia came into use as a fertilizer. Injury has been due primarily to accidental spillage

---

TABLE F-V

Sensitivity of selected plants to ammonia[a]

Sensitive

Mustard	Sunflower
Brassica juncea, Coss.	*Helianthus annuus*, L.

Intermediate

Buckwheat	Grass, annual blue	Tobacco
Fagopyrum esculentum, Moench.	*Poa annua*, L.	*Nicotiana tabacum*, L.
Cheeseweed	Grass, Kentucky blue	Tomato
Malva rotundifolia, L.	*Poa pratensis*, L.	*Lycopersicon esculentum*, Mill.
Coleus	Lambs-quarters	
Coleus, sp.	*Chenopodium album*, L.	

Resistant

Apple (fruit)	Dandelion	Peach (fruit)
Malus, sp.	*Taraxacum officinale*, Weber	*Prunus persica*, Sieb. & Zucc.
Chickweed	Nettle-leaf goosefoot	Pigweed
Cerastium, sp.	*Chenopodium murale*, L.	*Aramanthus retroflexus*, L.

aListing of plants came from references 1, 7, 30, and personal observations of A. S. Heagle.

or start-up of industrial operations, since continuous ammonia release from industrial plants is not sufficiently high to cause acute injury symptoms. Ammonia has not received extensive or critical study under laboratory conditions.

Relative Susceptibility

Thornton and Setterstrom[7] have reported injury to buckwheat, coleus, sunflower, and tomato foliage after a 1-hr exposure to 40 ppm and slight marginal injury after a 4-hr exposure to 16.6 ppm ammonia.

Levels required to produce injury were about ten times greater than those reported for sulfur dioxide and were somewhat comparable to those reported for nitrogen dioxide and hydrochloric acid. The relative susceptibilities for several species are shown in Table F-V.

Symptomatology

Injury reported from laboratory exposures has consisted of acute tissue collapse, with or without subsequent loss of chlorophyll. Leaves show a cooked green appearance, becoming brown or perhaps staying green on drying. Benedict and Breen[1,2] reported necrotic spotting primarily along the leaf margins in sensitive weed species. Field observations from ammonia spills have reported extensive and widespread injury within 1-2 miles of the spill. A complete collapse of leaf tissue occurs close to the source with the tissue turning black overnight. Several sensitive species show blackened tissue at distances up to a mile from the spill. Sulfur dioxide-type lesions are seen on many sensitive species but the necrotic areas turn a bright tan instead of a white color (Figures F-20 thru F-22). Several cereals and grasses have shown necrotic and chlorotic interveinal streaking at some distance from the spill. A light to bright red to purple pigmentation is often associated with this streaking on monocot leaves. Several species show an upper-surface glazing with or without scattered necrotic spotting (Figure F-19).

Brennan et al.[36] exposed several varieties of peach and apple fruits to ammonia after a break in an ammonia line in a large storage area caused severe fruit injury. A purple to black discoloration occurred around the lenticels of apple fruits (Figure F-23) fumigated with 300 ppm of ammonia, which disappeared when fumigations were discontinued. The discoloration persisted when concentrations above 400 ppm were used. Peaches developed an over-all blackening which faded at lower concentrations (200 ppm). Symptoms in both fruits were characteristic of those reported in the storage area.

Hydrogen Chloride

Hydrogen chloride is not considered to be of major concern except from isolated industrial processes. It was first reported over a century ago as causing extensive injury to vegetation around the Le Blanc soda factories in England and Germany.[38] The injury extended as much as a half mile from the source and resulted from exposures to hydrogen chloride generated by the treatment of salt with sulfuric acid. The problem of vegetation injury was solved by the installation of scrubbers that effectively removed the gas.

Injury has recently been related to incineration of polyvinyl chlorides.[37] Field injury occurred in vegetation within a half mile of the open burning source. The burning of any chlorine-containing organic compounds would be expected to yield hydrogen chloride.

Field observations have been minimal in the United States because the concentrations necessary to produce injury rarely occur.

Symptomatology and Relative Susceptibility

Hydrogen chloride will cause an acid-type necrotic lesion at concentrations similar to those which cause injury by ammonia. The reaction is thought to be a pH response in plant tissue. No chronic or growth effects have been reported for this pollutant.

Hasselhoff and Lindau[37] reported that Viburnum and larch seedlings were killed in less than 2 days by exposure to 5-20 ppm of hydrogen chloride. They also reported that hydrochloric acid fumes resulted in bleached lesions and necrotic margins in deciduous trees, and that this gas produced local lesions on fir, beech, and oak after a 1-hr fumigation with 1,000 ppm of the gas. Tipburn of fir needles was noted 3 weeks after two exposures to hydrogen chloride gas at 1,000 ppm. Necrosis along the leaf margins of maple, birch and pear resulted from 1-hr daily exposures to 2,000 ppm HCl for 80 days.

Shriner and Lacasse[39] exposed 28-day old Bonny Best tomato plants to 5 ppm of hydrogen chloride for 2 hrs. These

---

TABLE F-VI

Sensitivity of selected plants to hydrogen chloride[a]

Sensitive

Beet, sugar *Beta vulgaris*, L.	Larch *Larix*, sp.	Tomato *Lycopersicon esculentum*, Mill.
Cherry *Prunus*, sp.	Maple *Acer*, sp.	Viburnum *Viburnum*, sp.

Intermediate

Begonia *Begonia rex*, Putz.	Rose *Rosa*, sp. Rosebud *Rosa*, sp.	Spruce *Picea*, sp.

Resistant

Beech *Fagus*, sp.	Maple *Acer*, sp.	Pear *Pyrus*, sp.
Birch *Betula*, sp.	Oak *Quercus*, sp.	Spruce *Picea*, sp.
Fir *Abies*, sp.		

[a]Listing of plants came from references 37, 39, and 40.

plants developed interveinal bronzing followed by necrosis within 72 hrs of the exposure. Analysis of plant tissue showed large increases of titratable chlorides in the fumigated plants. The immature leaves showed the greatest increase in chlorides and the least sensitivity to the pollutant.

Means and Lacasse[40] report the fumigation of twelve tree species, 2-5 years old, with 3-43 ppm of hydrogen chloride for a period of 4 hrs.

Field injury from hydrochloric acid fumes have been reported from several sources.[37,38] Marginal necrosis and leaf spotting are shown in Figures F-24 and F-25. Table F-VI gives relative species susceptibility.

Mercury

In 1797 four Dutch chemists discovered that metallic mercury vapors might injure foliage of plants. In 1867 Boussingault[41] demonstrated that vapors from mercury had a deleterious effect on plants. Ratsek[42] and Zimmerman and Crocker[43] reported that mercury vapors from bichloride of mercury mixed with soil produced injury to rose foliage throughout the greenhouse. Butterfield[44] reported injury to roses from the mercury in anti-mildew paint. At present, mercury phytotoxicity is rare since it has largely been replaced in paint and in soil treatments by organic fungicides and nematocides that do not contain mercury.

Symptomatology and Relative Susceptibility

Mercury will cause chlorosis, abscission of older leaves, growth reduction, and general poor growth and develop-ment. Injury is usually restricted to greenhouse crops, where effects are pronounced.[44] Levels necessary to produce injury to sensitive plants have not been documented because research did not include air monitoring. Probably levels in the ppb range applied over several days are necessary for injury to occur.

Zimmerman and Crocker[43] reported that mercury vapors caused floral injury to Briarcliff roses. The flowers developed characteristic faded pink petals (Figure F-26) occasionally showing varying amounts of brown. Buds may fail to open and the corollas may abscise from the receptacle. The stamens of the injured buds usually varied from dark brown to nearly black in color. A difference in varietal susceptibility was noted.

Fumigations demonstrated that floral parts were more sensitive to low concentrations of mercury vapors than leaves, and that older leaves were more responsive than immature ones. Hitchcock and Zimmerman[45] reported that mercury vapors from paint resulted in the development of curvature and stiffness of the leaflets. The veins of the leaves prematurely turned yellow or brown and defoliation was common.

Peach seedlings were found to be very susceptible to mercury vapors.[43] The first signs of injury were the fading and subsequent browning of interveinal tissue on the older leaves. With mild exposures, many brown spots appeared first on the older leaves and then more generally over the plant with the youngest leaves being most resistant. Abscission of injured leaves occurred, especially at low tempera-

F8

TABLE F-VII

Sensitivity of selected plants to mercury vapor[a]

Sensitive

Bean
  Phaseolus, sp.
Butterflyweed
  Asclepias tuberosa, L.
Cinquefoil
  Potentilla, sp.
Fern, Boston
  Nephrolepis exaltata, Schott.
  Var. *bostoniensis Davenport*

Fern, holly
  Cyrtomium falcatum, Smith
Hydrangea
  Hydrangea, sp.
Mimosa
  Mimosa, sp.
Oxalis
  Oxalis, sp.

Privet
  Ligustrum, sp.
Sunflower
  Helianthus, sp.
Willow
  Salix, sp.

Intermediate

Azalea
  Rhododendron, sp.
Basswood (seedling)
  Tilia, sp.
Begonia
  Begonia, sp.
Camellia
  Camellia, sp.
Columbine
  Aquilegia, sp.
Cosmos
  Cosmos, sp.
Cotoneaster
  Cotoneaster, sp.
Forsythia
  Forsythia, sp.
Fuchsia
  Fuchsia, sp.

Geranium
  Geranium, sp.
Holly, American
  Ilex opaca, Ait.
Lily, Calla
  Zantedeschia aethiopica, Spreng.
Lily, Easter
  Lilium harrisii, Carr.
Maple, Japanese
  Acer palmatum, Thumb.
Oak
  Quercus, sp.
Peach
  Prunus persica, Sieb. & Zucc.
Persimmon
  Diospyros virginiana, L.
Pine, white
  Pinus strobus, L.

Privet
  Ligustrum, sp.
Salvia
  Salvia, sp.
Saxifrage
  Saxifrage, sp.
Strawberry
  Fragaria, sp.
Tobacco
  Nicotiana, sp.
Tomato
  Lycopersicon esculentum, Mill.
Viburnum
  Viburnum, sp.
Vinca
  Vinca, sp.

Resistant

Aloe
  Aloe, sp.
Cherry, Jerusalem
  Solanum pseudocapsicum, L.

Croton
  Codiaeum, sp.
Holly, Chinese
  Ilex Chinensis, Loes

Ivy
  Hedera, sp.
Sarcococca
  Sarcococca, sp.

[a]Listing of plants came from references 32 and 43.

tures. At high temperatures injury was more severe. Privet response to mercury vapors was similar to that of the peach except that green leaves frequently fell without signs of injury to the blade.

Forty-two plant species studied to determine relative sensitivity to mercury[43] are listed in Table F-VII according to their sensitivity when exposed for 72 hrs.

Particulates (including heavy metals and sulfuric acid mist)

Particulate emissions are not generally considered to be harmful to vegetation unless they are highly caustic or heavy deposits occur. Many particulates are by-products of agricultural practices and are usually inert. Alkaline particulates from cement manufacture may produce injury close to the source.[46] High particulate emissions close to quality fruit- and vegetable-producing areas have coated the vegetable and fruit products and caused a reduction in quality or an increase in labor costs for cleaning. Lime deposits are known to form encrustations on leaves of vegetation with a resultant reduction in photosynthesis, vigor and hardiness of the plants. However, particulates are not considered to be phytotoxic pollutants of major importance.

Heavy metal contaminates have not been generally accepted as air pollutants. However, we are becoming more concerned with these as aerosol pollutants, since they may produce an effect on vegetation close to the source. The heavy metals of general interest include lead, manganese, zinc, nickel, boron, beryllium and cadmium. Since sources of these include gasoline additives, they are found in auto exhaust. Several studies along highly-traveled roadways have associated the lead content of vegetation with adsorption of lead from automobile exhaust,[47,48] thus producing a potential hazard to human health. Although lead levels close to highways have been high, injury symptoms on vegetation have been lacking. There is some concern that marginal burn on leaves in urban areas might be associated with heavy metal contamination from auto exhaust. Preliminary analyses have shown high nickel, manganese, and boron content in some of this dead and injured vegetation.[49] Although much of the injury along city streets is associated with salt injury from winter applications, preliminary analyses suggest that some injury is also associated with the heavy metals from auto exhaust.

Laboratory and field studies have shown that sulfur dioxide may be oxidized to sulfur trioxide under conditions which occur in ambient air. This trioxide rapidly hydrates, forming small airborne droplets of sulfuric acid (mist) which vary in size with the relative humidity. Humidity, sunlight, catalytic particulate matter, hydrocarbons, and oxides of nitrogen increase the speed of conversion of sulfur dioxide to the trioxide. It has not yet been determined whether the sulfuric acid thus formed directly affects plants in nature, however, Middleton et al.[50,51] have reported necrotic spots on the upper surface of foliage in the Los Angeles area following foggy periods and Thomas et al.[52] produced upper-surface necrotic spotting from sulfuric acid mist on moist leaf surfaces.

TABLE F-VIII

Sensitivity of selected plants to hydrogen sulfide[a]

Sensitive

Aster	Cucumber	Salvia
Aster macrophyllus, L.	*Cucumis sativus*, L.	*Salvia*, sp.
Bean, kidney	Lamb's quarters	Soybean
Phaseolus vulgaris, L.	*Chenopodium album*, L.	*Glycine max.*, Merr.
Buckwheat	Nettle-leaf goosefoot	Tobacco
Fagopyrum esculentum, Moench	*Chenopodium murale*, L.	*Nicotiana glauca*, Grah.
Calliopsis	Poppy	Tobacco, Turkish
Calliopsis, sp.	*Papaver somniferum*, L.	*Nicotiana tabacum*, L.
Clover	Radish	Tomato
Trifolium, sp.	*Raphanus sativus*, L.	*Lycopersicon esculentum*, Mill.
Cosmos		
Cosmos bipinnatus, Cau.		

Intermediate

Castor bean	Gladiolus	Pepper
Ricinus communis, L.	*Gladiolus*, sp.	*Capsicum frutescens*, L.
Chickweed	Grass, Kentucky blue	Rose
Stellaria media, Cyrill.	*Poa pratensis*, L.	*Rosa*, sp.
Cornflower	Nasturtium	Sunflower
Centaurea cyanus, L.	*Tropaeolum majas*, L.	*Helianthus annuus*, L.
Dandelion		
Taraxacum officinale, Weber		

Resistant

Apple	Fern, Boston	Pigweed
Malus pumila, Mill.	*Nephrolepis exaltata*, Schott var.	*Amaranthus retroflexus*, L.
Carnation	*bostoniensis*, Davenport	Purslane
Dianthus caryophyllus, L.	Grass, annual blue	*Portulaca oleracea*, L.
Cheeseweed	*Poa annua*, L.	Strawberry
Malva parviflora, L.	Mustard	*Fragaria*, sp.
Cherry	*Brassica campestris*, L.	
Prunus serotina, Ehrhe.	Peach	
Coleus	*Prunus persica*, Sieb. & Zucc.	
Coleus blumei, Benth.		

[a]Listing of plants came from references 1 and 53.

Hydrogen Sulfide

Hydrogen sulfide, a natural product of decay, is found as a normal swamp gas, and is a by-product of certain industrial processes. Field injury has not been reported from hydrogen sulfide. The absence of literature on hydrogen sulfide injury to plants reflects the relative unimportance of this gas as a phytotoxic air pollutant. Elemental sulfur (wettable sulfur powders), calcium or sodium polysulfides, and polysulfide compounds have been widely used as fungicides. These fungicides possess pronounced phytotoxic properties especially when the air temperature is high.

Laboratory exposures[1,52] produced scorching of the young shoots and leaves, with basal and marginal scorching of the next oldest leaves. Mature leaves were unaffected. Symptoms were usually fully expressed within a few days of the treatment. When injury was not too intense, it tended to be interveinal. This is the only pollutant known to affect the growing tip of sensitive plants, although PAN is generally associated with young tissue. McCallan et al.[53] reported a marked variation in the response of twenty-nine species to fumigation with hydrogen sulfide. The most sensitive plants used developed slight injury after exposures below 40 ppm whereas the most resistant ones failed to show visible injury to an exposure of 400 ppm for 5 hrs. Relative sensitivities are shown in Table F-VIII.

Toxic levels are well above known ambient concentrations. Chronic symptoms and growth effects are unreported. McCallan et al.[53] reported that temperature and soil moisture were important environmental factors relating to sensitivity of vegetation to hydrogen sulfide.

Carbon Monoxide

Carbon monoxide is a product of incomplete combustion and is generally associated with automobile exhaust. It has undergone only brief laboratory study.[54] Injury similar to that shown with ethylene and other unsaturated gases was reported. Its effects may be the production of internal ethylene in plant tissue. Little is known about the effect of carbon monoxide on vegetation, but levels necessary to cause injury similar to ethylene are from 1,000 to 10,000 times higher than those reported for ethylene. These levels are well above reported ambient concentrations.

Discussion

The pollutants discussed in this chapter are of relatively less importance to vegetation than those discussed in the earlier chapters. Some of these pollutants are becoming more prevalent and may become increasingly important as more is learned about plant response to them. Several of the pollutants will also increase in importance as they become more widely used in the United States. Most of these pollutants are known to come from specific sources and the injury reported from them has usually been of an acute type. When pollutants come from specific sources, if an experienced observer knows the source and type of pollutant with which he is dealing, the plant injury should be recognizable from the acute symptoms; there should be no interfering or mimicking symptoms which could confuse the investigator except those from other air pollutants. Thus for most of the specific pollutants listed the cause will probably be well defined. For those pollutants which do not come from specific sources, the variety of mimicking symptoms and interfering diagnoses discussed for the four major pollutants would hold. Interactions and effects of environmental conditioning, species and varietal susceptibility, potential interactions with other pollutants and pathogenic organisms have not been studied in relation to these other phytotoxic pollutants.

References

1. Benedict, H. M. and Breen, W. H., "Development of standards for evaluating vegetation damage caused by air pollution," *Stanford Res. Inst. Tech. Rept.*, **11**, (Dec. 1955).
2. Benedict, H. M. and Breen, W. H., "The use of weeds as a means of evaluating vegetation damage caused by air pollution," *Proc. 3rd Natl. Air Pollution Symp.*, 177-190, Pasadena, Calif. (1955).
3. Brandt, C. S. and Heck, W. W., "Effects of air pollutants on vegetation," in *Air Pollution*, 2 ed., Stern, vol. 1, 401-443, Academic Press, New York (1969).
4. Crocker, W., "Effect of certain lethal gases upon plants and animals," in *Growth of Plants*, 172-203, Reinhold Publ. Corp., New York (1948).
5. Thomas, M. D., "Gas damage to plants," *Ann. Rev. Plant Physiol.*, **2**, 293-322 (1951).
6. Thomas, M. D., "Effects of air pollution on plants," in *Air Pollution, World Health Organ., Monograph Ser.*, **46**, 233-278 (1961).
7. Thornton, N. C. and Setterstrom, C., "Toxicity of ammonia, chlorine, hydrogen cyanide, hydrogen sulfide, and sulfur dioxide gases. III. Green plants," *Contrib. Boyce Thompson Inst.*, **11**, 343-356 (1940).
8. Zimmerman, P. W., "Impurities of the air and their influence on plant life," *Proc. 1st. Natl. Air Pollution Symp.*, 135-141, Pasadena, Calif. (March 1950).
9. Crocker, W., "Physiological effects of ethylene and other carbon containing gases," in *Growth of Plants*, 139-171, Reinhold Publ. Corp., New York (1948).
10. Heck, W. W. and Pires, E. G., "Growth of plants fumigated with saturated and unsaturated hydrocarbon gases and their derivatives," *Texas Agr. Expt. Sta. Rept.*, **MP-603** (Aug. 1962).
11. Hall, C., Truchelut, G. B., Leinweber, C. L., and Herrero, F. A., "Ethylene production by the cotton plant and its effects under experimental and field conditions," *Physiol. Plantarum*, **10**, 306-317 (1957).
12. Zimmerman, P. W., Hitchcock, A. E. and Crocker, W., "Gas injury to roses in greenhouses," *Boyce Thompson Inst. Paper*, **20**, 198-209 (Oct. 1931).
13. Davidson, O. W., "Effects of ethylene on orchid flowers," *Proc. Am. Soc. Hort. Sci.*, **53**, 444-446 (1949).
14. Heck, W. W. and Pires, E. G., "Effect of ethylene on horticultural and agronomic plants," *Texas Agr. Expt. Sta., Rept.*, **MP-613** (Nov. 1962).
15. Smith, W. H., Parker, J. C., and Freeman, W. W., "Exposure of cut flowers to ethylene in the presence and absence of carbon dioxide," *Nature*, **211**, 99-100 (July 1966).
16. Altshuller, A. P., Klosterman, D. L., Leach, P. W., Hindawi, I. J., and Sigsby, J. E., "Products and biological effects from irradiation of nitrogen oxides with hydrocarbons or aldehydes under dynamic conditions," *Intern J. Air Water Pollution*, **10**, 81-98 (1966).
17. Darley, E. F., Burleson, F. R., Mateer, E. H., Middleton, J. T., and Osterli, V. P., "Contribution of burning of agricultural wastes to photochemical air pollution," *Air Pollution Control Assoc. Meetg, Papers*, **64-66** (June 1966).
18. Darley, E. F., Dugger, W. M., Mudd, J. B., Ordin, L., Taylor, O. C., and Stephens, E. R., "Plant damage by pollution derived from automobiles," *Arch. Environ. Health*, **6**, 761-770 (1963).
19. Haagen-Smit, A. J., Darley, E. F., Zaitlin, M., Hull, H., and Noble, W., "Investigation on injury to plants from air pollution in the Los Angeles area," *Plant Physiol.*, **27**, 18-34 (Jan. 1952).
20. Heck, W. W., "Plant injury induced by photochemical reaction products of propylene-nitrogen dioxide mixtures," *J. Air Pollution Control Assoc.*, **14**, 255-261 (1964).
21. Heck, W. W., "The use of plants as indicators of air pollution," *Intern. J. Air Water Pollution*, **10**, 99-111 (1966).
22. Hindawi, I. J., Dunning, J. A., and Brandt, C. S., "Morphological and microscopical changes in tobacco bean and petunia leaves exposed to irradiated automobile exhaust," *Phytopathology*, **55**, 27-30 (Jan. 1965).
23. Korth, M. W., "Effects of the ratio of hydrocarbon to oxides of nitrogen in irradiated auto exhaust," *Public Health Publ. (U.S.)*, **999-AP-20** (Oct. 1966).
24. Stephens, E. R., Darley, E. F., Taylor, O. C., and Scott, W. E., "Photochemical reaction products in air pollution," *Intern. J. Air Water Pollution*, **4**, 79-100 (1961).
25. Hammer, C. L. and Tukey, H. B., "The herbicidal action of 2,4-dichlorophenoxyacetic and 2,4,5-trichlorophenoxyacetic acid on bindweed," *Science*, **100**, 154-155 (1944).
26. Dunlap, A. A., "2,4-D injury to cotton from airplane dusting of rice," *Phytopathology*, **38**, 638-643 (1948).
27. Daines, R. H., "2,4-D as an air pollutant and its effects on various species of plants," in *Air Pollution, Proc. U. S. Tech. Conf. Air Pollution*, ed. McCabe, L. C., 140-143, McGraw-Hill, New York (1952).
28. Brennan, E., Leone, I. A., and Daines, R. H., "Chlorine as a phytotoxic air pollutant," *Intern. J. Air Water Pollution*, **9**, 791-797 (1965).
29. Brennan, E., Leone, I. A., and Daines, R. H., "Response of pine trees to chlorine in the atmosphere," *Forest Sci.*, **12**, 389-390 (1966).
30. Hindawi, I. J., "Injury by sulfur dioxide, hydrogen fluoride and chlorine as they were observed and reflected on vegetation in the field," *J. Air Pollution Control Assoc.*, **18**, 307-312 (1968).
31. Stout, G. L., "Chlorine injury to lettuce and other vegetation," *Calif. Dept. Agr. Bull.*, **21**, 340-344 (1932).
32. Zimmerman, P. W., "Chemicals involved in air pollution and their effects upon vegetation," *Prof. Papers Boyce Thompson Inst.*, **2**, 124-145 (1955).
33. Schmidt, H., "Beobachtung uber Gasschaden an Obstbaumen," *Deut. Baumsch.*, **3**, 10-12 (1951).
34. Brennan, E., Leone, I. A., and Holmes, C.,"Accidental chlorine gas damage to vegetation," *Plant Disease Reptr.*, **53**, 873-875 (1969).
35. Hill, A. C., personal communication (1969).
36. Brennan, E., Leone, I. A., and Daines, R. H., "Ammonia injury to apples and peaches in storage," *Plant Disease Reptr.*, **46**, 792-795 (1962).
37. Haselhoff, E. and Lindau, G., "Die Beschadigung der Vegetation durch Rauch," *Leipzig*, **11**, 203-256 (1903).
38. Lacasse, N. L., "Open burning and our forest: a new threat," *Forest Notes*, 23-25 (Summer 1968).
39. Shriner, D. A. and Lacasse, N. L., "Distribution of chlorides in tomato following exposure to hydrogen chloride gas," *Phytopathology*, **59**, 402 (abstr.) (1969).
40. Means, W. E., Jr., and Lacasse, N. L., "Relative sensitivity of twelve tree species to hydrogen chloride gas," *Phytopathology*, **59**, 401 (abstr.) (1969).
41. Boussingault, M., "Sur l'action deletere que la vapeur emanat' du mercure exerco sur les plants", *Acad. Sci.*, **64**, 924-929 (1867).
42. Ratsek, J. C., "Injury to roses from mercuric chloride used in soil for pests," *Florist Review*, **72**, 11-12 (1933).
43. Zimmerman, P. W. and Crocker, W., "Plant injury caused by vapors of mercury and compounds of mercury," *Contrib. Boyce Thompson Inst.*, **6**, 167-187 (1934).
44. Butterfield, N. W., "Roses affected by mercury compounds in greenhouse paint," *Florist Exchange, Hort. Trade World*, **123**, 14 (1954).
45. Hitchcock, A. E. and Zimmerman, P. W., "Toxic effects of vapors of mercury and of compounds of mercury on plants," *Anals. New York Acad. Sci.*, **65**, 474-497 (1957).
46. Darley, E. F., "Studies on the effect of cement-kiln dust on vegetation," *J. Air Pollution Control Assoc.*, **16**, 145-150 (1966).
47. Everett, J. L., Day, C. L. and Reynolds, D., "Comparative survey of lead and selected sites in the British Isles in relation to air pollution," *Food Cosmet. Toxicol.*, **5**, 29-35 (1967).
48. Martin, G. C. and Hammond, P. B., "Lead uptake by bromegrass from contaminated soils," *Agron J.*, **58**, 553-554 (1966).
49. McCabe, L., personal communication (1969).
50. Middleton, J. T., Darley, E. F., and Brewer, R. F., "Damage to vegetation from polluted atmosphere," *J. Air Pollution Control Assoc.*, **8**, 7-15 (1958).
51. Middleton, J. T., Kendrick, J. B., Jr., and Schwalm, H. W., "Injury to herbaceous plants by smog," *Plant Disease Reptr.*, **34**, 245-252 (1950).
52. Thomas, M. D., Hendricks, R. H., and Hill, G. R., Jr., "Some impurities in the air and their effects on plants," in *Air Pollution, Proc. U. S. Tech. Conf. Air Pollution*, ed. McCabe, L. C., McGraw-Hill, New York (1950).
53. McCallan, S. E. A., Hartzel, A., and Wilcoxon, F., "Hydrogen sulfide injury to plants", *Contrib. Boyce Thompson Inst.*, **8**, 189-197 (1936).
54. Zimmerman, P. W., "Anaesthetic properties of carbon monoxide and other gases in relation to plants, insects, and centipedes," *Contrib. Boyce Thompson Inst.*, **7**, 147-155 (1935).

Figure F-1. Dry sepal in orchid (*Orchis*, sp.) caused by ethylene in ambient air at about 0.1 ppm for 6 hrs. Flower on left shows severe necrosis of sepals after ethylene exposure. Flower on right was control grown in charcoal-filtered air. (Photo courtesy of E. F. Darley.)

F12

Figure F-2. Ethylene injury to rose (*Rosa*, sp.) obtained in the laboratory. The younger leaves and stem show severe epinasty. The older leaves show a general loss of chlorophyll with more prominent interveinal chlorosis. (Photo courtesy of O. W. Davidson.)

Figure F-3. Auto exhaust injury to Bel-W3 tobacco (*Nicotiana,* sp.) produced in the laboratory by 1.5 hrs. exposure to 0.25 ppm oxidant. Severe injury on the younger leaves was caused by a combination of PAN and type-3 injury. The severe injury on the lower leaves was caused by ozone. The fleck or necrotic lesions shown on the oldest leaf are probably caused by a combination of the three pollutants with no PAN-type injury evident.

Figure F-4. Ambient oxidant injury to muskmelon (*Cucumis melo,* L.) observed in the field. Oldest leaves are affected first. Injury is initiated as a diffuse chlorotic mottle on the upper surface which steadily deepens until the leaf is practically white. Green tissue along the veins has a netted appearance in the injury pattern. Injury is common throughout the Atlantic Coast areas and major Eastern cities.

Figure F-5. Ambient oxidant injury to alfalfa (*Medicago sativa,* L.) observed in the field. Injury shows as light tan necrotic lesions scattered throughout the leaflets, primarily interveinal. Similarly located but pigmented lesions are also common. Injury is common in the Los Angeles basin.

F14

Figure F-6. Ambient oxidant injury to red clover (*Trifolium pratense,* L.) observed in the field. Injury occurs as general necrotic lesions, rust red in color, primarily interveinal in location, with little edgeburn. Injury was noted in Cincinnati, Ohio.

Figure F-7. Ambient oxidant injury to grapefruit (*Citrus,* sp.) observed in the field. Symptoms are initiated as a fading of normal green color, to mild and more intensive chlorosis, to complete leaf chlorosis and the leaf drop. Symptoms are found extensively in the Los Angeles basin. (Photo courtesy of O. C. Taylor.)

F15

Figure F-8. Arsenic trioxide injury to lilac (*Syringa vulgaris,* L.) observed in the field. Spray drift from arsenic trioxide showing discrete necrotic lesions, as if sprayed with liquid drops. The lighter center with darker borders is characteristic of this symptom. (Photo courtesy of A. C. Hill.)

Figure F-9. Atrazine injury to soybean (*Glycine max.* Merr.) observed in the field. A residual soil application of atrazine resulted in diffuse necrotic lesions and chlorotic development, primarily interveinal with some edgeburn. This indicates the sensitivity of soybean to this herbicide. Symptoms may be confused with ozone or ambient oxidant. (Photo courtesy of T. W. Barrett.)

Figure F-10. 2,4-D injury to cotton (*Gossypium,* sp.) observed in the field. A typical response of cotton to drift of a 2,4-D type of spray. Injury is common throughout areas where cotton is within 2-15 miles of areas receiving aerial applications of **2,4-D** type herbicide esters, especially when applications **are applied during poor** weather conditions. (Photo courtesy of T. W. Barrett.)

Figure F-11. Chlorine injury to mustard (*Brassica*, sp.) observed in the field. The general pattern of injury is similar to that reported on some species by ozone. Complete collapse of the older leaves is noted with severe necrosis starting at the tips and working down in the younger leaves. The youngest leaves are unaffected. The less seriously injured tissue shows only upper-surface lesions. (Photo courtesy of O. C. Taylor.)

Figure F-12. Chlorine injury to soybean (*Glycine max*, Merr.) produced in the laboratory with 6 ppm for 10 min. Injury occurs as a severe edge necrosis combined with upper-surface necrotic lesions occasionally extending through the leaf. Lesions show heavy pigmentation. The pattern is somewhat dissimilar to that normally associated with ozone in that the lesions tend to run together and do not remain as small individual lesions. (Photo courtesy of O. C. Taylor.)

Figure F-13. Chlorine injury to Italian prune (*Prunus domestica*, L.) observed in the field. Injury appears primarily as an upper-surface bleach or scattered non-pigmented necrotic lesions. Scattered severe lesions are seen which extend through the leaf. This injury could be confused with that associated with ozone. (Photo courtesy of A. C. Hill.)

F18

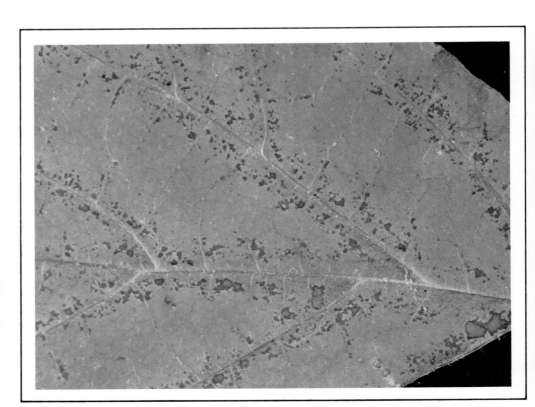

Figure F-14. Chlorine injury to witch hazel (*Hamamelis virginiana*, L.) observed in the field. The discrete necrotic lesions located primarily along the veins, and extending through the leaf are common symptoms. Lesions are colored a light to dark reddish-tan. The intercostal necroses may or may not be concentrated along the veins depending on environmental conditions during exposure. (Photo courtesy of A. C. Hill.)

Figure F-15. Chlorine injury to elm (*Ulmus,* sp.) observed in the laboratory with 13 ppm for 10 min. Chlorine does not usually show the diffuse to severe chlorotic development which appears in this picture. The exposed plant on the right also shows some reddish-tan necrotic lesions in interveinal parts of some of the leaves. Symptoms are comparable to those observed in the field following an accidental spill. (Photo courtesy of O. C. Taylor.)

F19

Figure F-16. Chlorine injury to ginkgo (*Ginkgo biloba,* L.) observed in the field. Injury appears as a light bleach on the upper surface of the leaves, which might be confused with ozone type of injury. (Photo courtesy of A. C. Hill.)

Figure F-17. Chlorine injury to larch (*Larix*, sp.) observed in the field. Injury appears as a light to heavy chlorotic needle mottle. The type of injury and the pattern are similar to that shown on white pine which is injured by the oxidant-sulfur dioxide combination. (Photo courtesy of A. C. Hill.)

F20

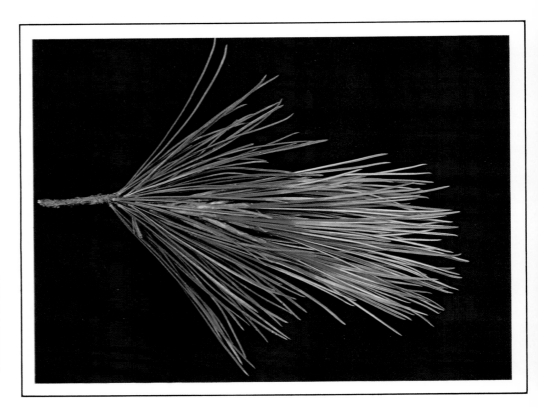

Figure F-18. Chlorine injury to white pine (*Pinus strobus*, L.) observed in the field. Injury appears as a light to reddish-tan necrosis of needle tips. Symptoms are generally lighter than tipburn caused by other pollutants. Light chlorotic mottle is seen on intact portions of the needles. (Photo courtesy of A. C. Hill.)

Figure F-19. Ammonia injury to dandelion (*Taraxacum officinale,* Weber) observed in the field. Injury is primarily an upper-surface glaze with development of some reddish-purple pigmentation. Some necrotic lesions extend through the leaf thickness. Glaze is more pronounced on the younger leaves. (Photo courtesy of A. C. Hill.)

F21

Figure F-20. Ammonia injury to cotton (*Gossypium,* sp.) observed in the field. Injury is shown as scattered necrotic lesions primarily interveinal, which extend through the leaf. Lesions could be confused with sulfur dioxide injury but they tend to have a tan to reddish-tan cast unlike the sulfur dioxide lesions. (Photo courtesy of T. W. Barrett.)

Figure F-21. Ammonia injury to corn (*Zea mays,* L.) observed in the field. Severe injury to corn shows primarily as an edge necrotic streaking with some interveinal streaking and necrotic spotting. Injury is similar to that caused by sulfur dioxide except for the pronounced reddish-tan coloration of the necrotic areas.

F22

Figure F-22. Ammonia injury to rye (*Secale cereale,* L.) grass observed in the field. Injury is similar to that found in corn but also exhibits some light to rather severe chlorosis with some purple pigmentation.

Figure F-23. Ammonia injury to apple (*Malus*, sp.) observed in the laboratory with 300 ppm. The black spotting on the experimental apple is typical of the effect of high levels of ammonia on apple fruit. (Photo courtesy of Eileen Brennan.)

F23

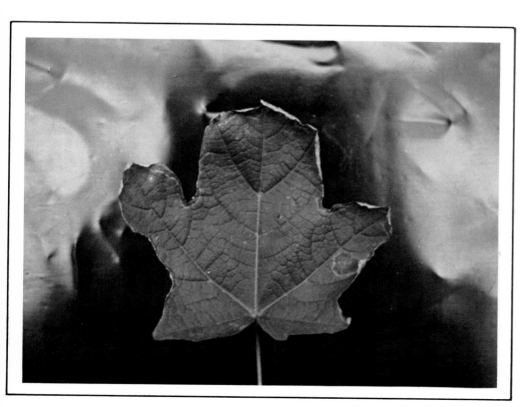

Figure F-24. Hydrogen chloride injury to maple (*Acer*, sp.) observed in the laboratory with 7 ppm for 4 hrs. Injury is observed primarily as a severe edge necrosis showing dark reddish-tan necrotic areas. (Photo courtesy of N. L. Lacasse.)

Figure F-25. Hydrogen chloride injury to cherry (*Prunus,* sp.) observed in the laboratory with 9 ppm for 4 hrs. Injury appears as typical acid spotting on the cherry leaf and is randomly distributed over the leaf surface. Necrotic lesions tend to be lighter in color than the edge necrosis on Norway Maple. (Photo courtesy of N. L. Lacasse.)

F24

Figure F-26. Mercury injury to rose (*Rosa,* sp.) observed in the greenhouse. Control roses are shown in the upper portion of the picture while the bleached flowers, caused by mercury, are shown in the lower portion of the picture. Three flower ages are included. (Photo courtesy of Boyce Thompson Institute.)

Field Surveys, Vegetation Sampling, and Air and Vegetation Monitoring

Leonard H. Weinstein
and
Delbert C. McCune
Boyce Thompson Institute for Plant Research, Yonkers, New York

Introduction

Controlled fumigations have provided much of our information on the appearance and consequence of air pollutant effects on plants. One practical use of these experimentally-derived data is their use together with field surveys, vegetation sampling and analysis, and ambient air monitoring in the evaluation and prevention of pollutant-induced injury or damage. However, field conditions differ considerably from the experimental situation and difficulties often arise in attempting to relate observed and reported behavior. For example, the type and severity or even the occurrence of pollutant-induced symptoms may be altered by biological factors such as genetic complement or stage of development of the plant, soil factors such as water or nutrient supply, or climatic factors such as temperature, light intensity or quality, relative humidity, or wind velocity (*e.g.,* see Heck[1] for factors affecting expression of symptoms of oxidant damage). In addition to the possible variability in symptom expression, biotic and abiotic factors can produce symptoms that mimic or mask those produced by the pollutant.[2,3] Many factors that affect symptom expression can also influence foliar accumulation of the pollutant and the relationship between air quality and the effect produced in the plant.[4] The problem in field surveillance, therefore, is the establishment of procedures and the acquisition of competency by personnel that will enable suitable information to be accumulated and evaluated.

General Considerations

Because of the complex nature of field evaluation, the individual responsible for the conduct of a survey should be a skilled observer and be able to recognize symptoms induced by pollutants, nutrient stresses or plant diseases, as well as being conversant with agronomy, horticulture, ecology, plant identification, the characteristics of emissions and their dispersion, air monitoring technology, and statistics. When unusual problems arise, someone with specialist knowledge of a supporting field may be required to participate in the survey.

The techniques employed in field surveys of vegetation, sampling of plant material for the accumulation of air-borne pollutants, and monitoring of air quality will be determined by two general considerations. The first is the type of data desired and the use that will be made of the information. Field surveys may be used, for example, for area planning and site evaluation prior to the installation of any facility which may represent a potential source of air contaminants, for determining the adequacy of existing control and abatement procedures by industry and by enforcement agencies, and for estimating injury or damage to vegetation in answer to a complaint or for purposes of arbitration or litigation. Secondly, any field operation will be dependent upon the amount of information already available on the area with respect to the amounts and types of emissions and characteristics of the source or sources, topographical and meteorological characteristics of the area, land use, the structure and composition of native vegetation, and the climatological and ecological characteristics of the area.

It should be apparent that no specific methods can be proposed which will be adequate for each of the problems that appears. Thus, the following discussion of field survey techniques will consider general features that are common to any survey. With these considerations in mind, a series of approaches can be formulated for area surveillance depending upon the nature of the problem and the limitations of the information and methods that may be available.

Field Surveys

The field survey is the most valuable means of periodically assessing the status of vegetation in areas where air pollution is a potential or real matter of concern. The survey must be carried out systematically and in such a manner that it relates directly to the problem and yields the maximum amount of useful information. The first step in the survey of vegetation is the determination of the probable or potential insult to vegetation by some type of emission inventory. Additionally, the probable amounts and the spatial and temporal distributions of the pollutants should be estimated from considerations of both the meteorological and topographical characteristics of the area and the operating characteristics of the sources.

Having accumulated as much information as possible on the pollutant and its dispersion, the potential receptors should be chosen by making a preliminary inventory in the field or after consulting a flora or field guide for the area from which the presence of plant species, their distribution and abundance, and their economic or aesthetic significance can be determined. Cole[5] has suggested five guidelines for the selection of indicator species: (1) the species should be sensitive to the pollutant at a level below the sensitivity of vegetation of economic or aesthetic importance; (2) it should be widely distributed; (3) the pollutant-induced markings should be characteristic and easily observed; (4) the species should be present throughout the growing season; and (5) the species should grow from a terminal shoot throughout the growing season. Benedict and Breen[6] selected and screened ten weed species based upon their prevalence in different areas of the country to determine a range of susceptibilities among the species with respect to different pollutants and the effect of water stress and stage of development upon susceptibility. Lichens and mosses may also serve as suitable indicators of industrial[7,8] or urban[9] pollution based on field observations of the relative abundance of certain species.

Surveillance procedures will generally follow those established by disciplines such as entomology, plant pathology, or forest mensuration, but with specific variations or procedures imposed by the nature of the air pollutant as an injurious factor. That is, the surveyor must be familiar with the appearance of pollutant-induced symptoms, the relative susceptibility of different species, and the ways in which biological and environmental factors can modify the expression of both plant symptoms and susceptibility (see preceding chapters). Thus, with a knowledge of the expected occurrence of the pollutant, a list of the species, symptoms, and environmental conditions can be compiled for suitable receptors which allows discrimination between the presence and absence of pollutant-induced effects in the area.

A degree of confusion and uncertainty may arise during the initial inspection of plants in the field even though the surveyor is thoroughly familiar with symptoms in photographs or from the results of experimental fumigations. This will be due to the fact that most vegetation will display symptoms of one type or another as a result of disease agents, insects, senescence, or environmental stresses such as heat, cold, drought, nutrient status, etc. Moreover, variation in symptom expression for individual plants within a single species may be very great. The problem, therefore, is to acquire specific information in such a way that general patterns will become apparent. Thus, the sites to be surveyed, the size of the quadrat at each site, and the description of the vegetation must be systematic and sufficient to be representative of the area and the conditions that prevail.

Considerable latitude can be allowed in the exact location of survey sites since they may vary in accessibility and the abundance of potential receptors. However, the sites should be selected in such a manner that they can be located on a topographic map or other chart; they should be sufficiently numerous and well dispersed so that effects due to pollution can be distinguished from other local effects; and they should contain a reasonable number of indicator plants at each site, preferably of the same species, but if this is not possible, ones whose ranges overlap at some of the sites.

The method of survey at the observational site may vary with the surveyor and other factors. The use of quadrats or the type of transect used to sample vegetation, the number and size of the quadrats, or the length and interval of the transect should be consistent with sound ecological methods.[10] The methods chosen will undoubtedly reflect a number of compromises. For example, the sites will be small enough and sufficiently few in number that the cost of survey is not excessive but large and numerous enough so that false conclusions as to differences in the abundance of symptoms from one site to another will not result from random or, perhaps, periodic variation.

The symptoms on the plants must be observed and described with respect to a qualitative estimate of their severity, and the frequency and variability of their occurrence for the individual species and among different species. The description of the symptoms should be accurate and sufficiently detailed to allow the causal agent and probable circumstances of exposure to be determined; however, a lengthy and time-consuming report is not necessary if the observations are recorded systematically. For example, in addition to identification and description of the site, the report should include: (1) species; (2) type of marking; (3) age of foliage affected; (4) distribution of the symptoms on the leaf; (5) the surface of the leaf affected; and (6) distribution of symptoms over the entire plant. In addition, photographic records should be made. Probably the most extensive survey was that conducted by agricultural specialists throughout California. Four categories of crops and eight species of weeds were rated for the absence or presence of pollutant-induced damage and the results were reported in a form suitably detailed for electronic data processing.[11]

The guidelines suggested for the selection of indicator species are, for the most part, obvious, but the reasons for selecting a plant of indeterminate growth habit may not be readily apparent. Plants of determinate and indeterminate growth will present different aspects concerning the circumstances of exposure. There is a period in the life of the leaf at which it is most susceptible to a given pollutant. Thus the appearance of markings on leaves of plants of determinate growth will serve to locate at least one time of exposure and may help to discriminate between the effects of several pollutants. However, indeterminate growth, with continual development of leaves, can furnish a historical record of exposures. It should be noted that pollutants such as fluoride may be exceptions due to their accumulative nature in the plant. Thus, some latency may occur in the manifestation of exposure conditions depending upon the accumulation of the pollutant and the environmental situation.

Clearly, more information is necessary if distinction is to be made between the effects of air pollution and other biotic and abiotic factors. The foliage, stems, and roots should be carefully inspected for signs of insect or mite activity and fungal, bacterial, or viral lesions, and cankers. Hepting and Berry[12] have provided information in tabular form which will be helpful in differentiating among the needle blights of eastern white pine (*Pinus strobus,* L). If the observational site contains different habitats, comparisons can be made to determine if environmental factors may be of consequence and the conditions of the vegetation can be evaluated with respect to general climatic records. The surveyor should also determine whether his observations generally conform to published information on relative susceptibilities of the indigenous vegetation. If meteorological and air monitoring data are available, the biological effects should be compared with the expected exposure conditions. There is also the possibility that a condition will be observed where no specific agent or factor can be distinguished as the cause. For example, damage to eastern white pine by semi-mature-tissue needle blight[13] or post-emergence chronic tipburn[14] have been extensively investigated but their etiologies still remain unknown.

Vegetation Sampling

Two different uses have been made of vegetation sampling. In some areas it has furnished a general and relative index of pollution, such as the foliar accumulation of sulfate[15] around industrialized areas. It has also been used to monitor the accumulation of toxic or potentially toxic pollutants in crops destined for human or livestock consumption, e.g., fluoride, nuclides, beryllium, lead, and pesticides. The latter use is probably more relevant today since other static and cumulative methods for air monitoring

G2

are available, which are more economical and reliable than vegetation sampling.

The cost of vegetation sampling and analysis and the degree of detail and reliability desired in the results will probably determine the methods to be used. Kaudy et al.[16] reported least significant differences (5% level) for fluoride levels in citrus leaves of about 12-30% of the mean due to analytical variation and about 15% for field sampling variation with leaves of adjacent trees. Generally, vegetation sampling must be regarded as an exercise in quality control and thus the optimum strategy will reflect statistical and economic considerations. However, the nature and location of the vegetation that is sampled will be determined by the expected dispersion patterns of the pollutants and the occurrence and use of the appropriate receptor.

Although theory may dictate the sampling scheme and the location of sampling sites, the biological or agronomic characteristics of the vegetation will determine the amount and type of samples to be taken. The sample should be representative of the vegetation in question. For example, for timothy-red clover, orchard grass-alfalfa, or other mixtures of species in forage, the same relative masses of the different species should be taken as occur in the local area which is sampled. This also applies to the different growth habits and ages of an individual species. The sampling should also discriminate with respect to the portion of the plant that will be of consequence, e.g., the whole corn (Zea mays, L.) plant when it is used for silage, or the ear when that part will be used for livestock or human consumption. Similarly, the height at which the forage is normally mowed should be reflected in the acquisition of a sample. Care should be taken in the selection of sample locations that the areas are remote from other sources of contamination, such as road dust. In addition, the samples should be kept free of soil particles.

Since most forage sampling will be carried out to conform with a standard, it is imperative that samples be taken from areas under active production. Thus, samples should be representative of the crop before cutting and after subsequent regrowth. It is realized that within this scheme samples may be taken from an area under production but still may not be representative of the product which is presented to the consumer. The cost of sampling a periodically-harvested crop just before each harvest would be quite expensive and cumbersome. Thus, routine and periodic surveys may sample young regrowth that has been recently exposed to a contaminant and find a level considerably higher than that which would have been found after dilution by subsequent growth and loss of foliar tissue or by weathering. The sample, however, does furnish information that an episode has occurred and that action may be necessary in order to prevent future occurrences.

The number of sampling sites within a field or portion of a field and the number of samples taken from a single site depend upon biological and ecological variation, distribution of the pollutant, and the precision of the methods used for subsequent analysis. Thus, the number of samples cannot be fixed but must be great enough to represent the field populations and to allow decisions to be made with a desired degree of confidence. Specific practices cannot be recommended for vegetation sampling and analysis in connection with standards and air quality, since the methods to be used will probably be established as part of a standard. Moreover, standards that are to be established should specify the means by which environmental quality will be determined.

Air Sampling and Analysis

It is evident that the efficacy of air quality standards depends upon the methods of air quality measurement since the ability of industry to comply with standards and to judge the effectiveness of control measures will be possible only by the use of air monitoring methods. Atmospheric monitoring may be the only sufficiently rapid and sensitive method for the detection and subsequent prevention of potentially harmful levels of pollutants. The importance of the information derived from air sampling demands that considerable care should be exercised in the selection of equipment, sites, and procedures. In choosing sites to define the air quality of an air shed or a region, the locations may be a fixed grid, as for example in the Polk County, Florida, survey described by Hendrickson,[17] or with a definite plan of movement, and will depend upon their relationship to topographic and meteorological factors. Thus, either permanent sites may be chosen with appropriate meteorological information or sites may be rotated according to some predetermined spatial or temporal scheme.

The equipment or analytical procedures employed should be appropriate to the use envisioned for them in terms of cost, portability, efficiency, selectivity, sensitivity, accuracy, precision, and reliability under field conditions. For example, if 24-hr mean concentrations are specified in a standard, an instrument capable of 30-min or shorter averaging periods will not be needed unless more information is desired on the dispersion patterns of the pollutant or the response of receptors to short-term peak concentrations. These methods will be evaluated by bodies such as The Intersociety Committee on a Manual of Ambient Air Sampling and Analysis[18] and established by enforcement agencies. The competency of the personnel involved in the sampling and analytical procedures is extremely important. It is also advisable to include some degree of meteorological monitoring with air sampling procedures if this has not already been established. Clearly, meteorological data will supplement and be extremely valuable in the interpretation and prediction of pollutant dispersion and plant damage.[19] Moreover Macdowell et al.[20] have shown that measurements of evapotranspiration and wind speed greatly improved the correlation of ozone concentration with weather fleck on tobacco.

Biological Monitors

As information on markings on native and cultivated plants is gathered from an area, it may be found to be incomplete due to inherent variability in susceptibility or insensitivity of the existing vegetation or to poor distribution of sensitive receptors. In this case, a bioassay technique may be necessary and biological monitors should be situated in field plots to supply the necessary information.[21,22] Gladiolus (Gladiolus, sp.),[23-25] and in one case, ponderosa pine seedlings (Pinus ponderosa, Laws),[23] have been used in several areas as biological monitors for air-borne fluorides because the amount of injury can be quantitatively determined and the plants are very sensitive to gaseous fluorides. The plots should be designed to fulfill the following criteria: (1) uniformity with respect to genetic background and cultural maintenance; (2) planted in sufficient abundance; (3) located at significant sites in the area with respect to pollutant dispersion; (4) composed of plants which will develop fairly specific symptoms to pollutants of interest; and (5) sufficient variety of plants at each site to represent a range of susceptibilities to a particular pollutant or to be specific for the different pollutants present. For example, several different factors were found to be involved in the development of annual bluegrass (Poa annua) as an indicator for smog concentrations in the Los Angeles basin. The characteristic symptoms were documented by controlled fumigation and field observation[26] and the effects of certain environmental factors on the susceptibility of the plant were determined.[27] A further refinement involved the use of special exposure chambers for the test plants.[28]

Certain guidelines should be followed to insure a reasonable amount of success: (1) select species and varieties that grow at least moderately well in the area; (2) conform with local cultural practices unless this is a part of a larger regional study where cultural conditions and the plant varieties have been standardized, as for example that reported by Heck et al;[29] (3) select sites of reasonable quality and those representative of conditions in the area within locations determined by pollutant dispersion and accessibility; (4) select the size of the plots and number of species per plot based upon the variability and degree of confidence desired in the results (estimates are frequently available as to the replication required for a difference of, e.g. 20%, to be significant). Some systematic scheme for the replacement of plants in the locations selected may be required if they are susceptible only during a certain period of their life cycle. This may be accomplished by using potted or in situ materials that are sown at periodic intervals. With potted plants, however, precautions should be taken to prevent water stress, nutritional imbalances, or excessive root temperatures. The sites should be inspected at weekly or more frequent intervals.

A refinement of biological monitoring is the use of "reverse fumigation" techniques where replicate plots or test objects are located at a given site. One set is enclosed and exposed to filtered air while the other is covered and exposed to the ambient air.[30,31] The major difficulties of this approach are the maintenance of the facilities, the great costs of establishing and maintaining suitable replication, and the effects of enclosure on the plants.

Although valuable information may be accrued from such biological monitors, they suffer from one major fault, i.e., field plots, like vegetation surveys, are after-the-fact and serve to confirm that injury has already occurred without revealing the more specific nature of the episode.

Acknowledgment

This review was supported in part by a grant from the National Air Pollution Control Administration, Consumer Protection and Environmental Health Service, U. S. Department of Health, Education, and Welfare, AP-00189.

References

1. Heck, W. W., "Factors influencing expression of oxidant damage to plants." Ann. Rev. Phytopathol., 6, 165-188 (1968).

2. Massey, L. M., "Similarities between disease symptoms and chemically induced injury to plants," in Air Pollution, Proc. U. S. Tech. Conf. Air Pollution, ed. McCabe, L. C., McGraw-Hill, New York (1952).

3. Treshow, M., "Evaluation of vegetation injury as an air pollution criterion," J. Air Pollution Control Assoc., 15, 266-269 (1965).

4. Pack, M. R. and Adams, D. F., "Problems of relating atmospheric analyses to effects of air pollution on agriculture," J. Air Pollution Control Assoc., 16, 219-324 (1966).

5. Cole, G. A., "Air pollution with relation to agronomic crops. III. Vegetation survey methods in air pollution studies," Agron. J., 50, 553-555 (1958).

6. Benedict, H. M. and Breen, W. H., "The use of weeds as a means of evaluating vegetation damage caused by air pollution," Proc. 3rd Natl. Air Pollution Symp., 177-190, Pasadena, Calif. (1955).

7. Gilbert, O. L., "Bryophytes as indicators of atmospheric pollution in the Tyne Valley," New Phytologist, 67, 15-30 (1968).

8. Rao, D. N. and LeBlanc, F., "Influence of an iron-sintering plant on Corticolous Epiphytes in Wawa, Ontario," Bryologist, 70, 141-157 (1967).

9. Skye, E., "Lichens and air pollution," Acta Phytogeographica Suecica, 52, 1-123 (1968).

10. Grieg-Smith, P., "Quantitative Plant Ecology," 2nd ed., Butterworth & Co., Washington (1964).

11. Middleton, J. T. and Paulus, A. O., "The identification and distribution of air pollutants through plant response," Arch. Ind. Health, 14, 526-532 (1956).

12. Hepting, G. H. and Berry, C. R., "Differentiating needle blights of white pine in the interpretation of fume damage," Intern. J. Air Water Pollution, 4, 101-105 (1961).

13. Linzon, S. N., "Damage to eastern white pine by sulfur dioxide, semimature-tissue needle blight, and ozone," J. Air Pollution Control Assoc., 16, 140-144 (1966).

14. Berry, C. R. and Hepting, G. H., "Injury to eastern white pine by unidentified atmospheric constituents," Forest Sci., 10, 2-13 (1964).

15. Bieberdorf, F. W., Shrewsbury, C. L., McKee, H. C., and Krough, L. H., "Vegetation as a measure indicator of air pollution. I. The pine (Pinus taeda)," Bull. Torrey Bot. Club, 85, 197-200 (1958).

16. Kaudy, J. C., Bingham, F. T., McColloch, R. C., Liebig, G. F., and Vanselow, A. P., "Contamination of citrus foliage by fluorine from air pollution in major California citrus areas," Proc. Am. Soc. Hort. Sci., 65, 121-127 (1955).

17. Hendrickson, E. R., "Dispersion and effects of air borne fluorides in Central Florida," J. Air Pollution Control Assoc., 11, 220-232 (1961).

18. Saltzman, B. E., "Air Quality Program needs uniform tests," Environ. Sci. Tech., 2, 22-32 (1968).

19. Adams, D. F., Mayhew, D. J., Gnagy, R. M., Richey, E. P., Koppe, R. W., and Allen, I. W., "Atmospheric pollution in the Ponderosa Pine blight area," Ind. Eng. Chem., 44, 1356-1365 (1952).

20. Macdowall, F. D. H., Mukammal, E. I., and Cole, A. F. W., "Direct correlation of air-polluting ozone and tobacco weather fleck," Can. J. Plant Sci., 44, 410-417 (1964).

21. Darley, E. F., "Use of plants for air pollution monitoring," J. Air Pollution Control Assoc., 10, 198-199 (1960).

22. Heck, W. W., "The use of plants as indicators of air pollution," Intern. J. Air Water Pollution, 10, 99-111 (1966).

23. Adams, D. F., Shaw, C. G., Gnagy, R. M., Koppe R. W., Mayhew, D. J., and Yerkes, W. D., Jr., "Relationship of atmospheric fluoride levels and injury indexes on gladiolus and ponderosa pine," J. Agr. Food Chem., 4, 64-66 (1956).

24. Compton, O. C. and Remmert, L. F., "Effect of air-borne fluorine on injury and fluorine content of gladiolus leaves," Proc. Am. Soc. Hort. Sci., 75, 663-675 (1960).

25. Miller, V. L., Allmendinger, D. F., Johnson, F., and Polley, D., "Lime papers and indicator plants in fluorine air pollution investigations," J. Agr. Food Chem., 1, 526-529 (1953).

26. Bobrov, R. A., "Use of plants as biological indicators of smog in the air of Los Angeles County," Science, 121, 510-511 (1955).

27. Juhren, M., Noble, W., and Went, F. W., "The standardization of Poa annua as an indicator of smog concentrations. I. Effects of temperature, photoperiod, and light intensity during growth of the test-plants," Plant Physiol., 32, 576-586 (1957).

28. Noble, W. M., and Wright, L. A., "Air pollution with relation to agronomic crops: II. A bio-assay approach to the study of air pollution," Agron. J., 50, 551-553 (1958).

29. Heck, W. W., Fox, F. L., Brandt, C. S., and Dunning, J. A., "Tobacco, a sensitive monitor for photochemical air pollution," Natl. Air Pollution Control Assoc. Contrib., 69-1 (1969).

30. Hindawi, I. J., "Injury by sulfur dioxide, hydrogen fluoride, and chlorine as they were observed and reflected on vegetation in the field," J. Air Pollution Control Assoc., 18, 307-312 (1968).

31. Thompson, C. R., Taylor, O. C., Thomas, M. D., and Ivie, J. O., "Effects of air pollutants on apparent photosynthesis and water use by citrus trees," Environ. Sci. Tech., 1, 644-650 (1967).

G4

Index of Plant Names

H2

PEPPER (*Capsicum,* sp.) F 5
PERIWINKLE (*Vinca,* sp.) E 4, E 7
PERSIMMON (*Diospyros virginiana,* L.) F 8
PETUNIA (*Petunia hybrida,* Vilm.) B 2, B 7, E 4, E 12, E 13, F 2, F 5
PHILODENDRON (*Philodendron cordatum,* Kunth.) F 2
PIGWEED (*Amaranthus retroflexus,* L.) D 3, F 5, F 9
PIGWEED (*Chenopodium,* sp.) E 2
PINE, Eastern white (*Pinus strobus,* L.) B 2, B 19, B 21, B 22, C 2, D 3, F 2, F 5, F 8, F 20, G 2
PINE, loblolly (*Pinus taeda,* L.) C 16, F 5
PINE, lodgepole (*Pinus contorta,* Dougl.), D 3
PINE, jack (*Pinus Banksiana,* Lamb.) F 5
PINE (*Mugho,* Turra.) D 3
PINE, ponderosa (*Pinus ponderosa,* Laws) B 2, B 20, B 21, C 2, D 3, D 8, D 14, G 3
PINE, Scotch (*Pinus sylvestris,* L.) D 3
PINE, shortleaf (*Pinus echinata,* Mill.) F 5
PINE, slash (*Pinus caribaea,* Morelet) F 5
PLANETREE (*Platanus,* sp.) D 3
PLANTAIN (*Plantago major,* L.) C 2
PLUM, Bradshaw (*Prunus domestica,* L.) D 3
PLUM, flowering (*Prunus cerasifera,* Ehrh.) D 3
POINSETTIA (*Poinsettia,* sp.) F 3
POLYGONUM (*Polygonum,* sp.) F 5
POPLAR, Carolina (*Populus eugenei,* Simon-Louis) D 3, D 10
POPLAR, lombardy (*Populus nigra,* L.) C 2, D 3
POPPY (*Papaver somniferum,* L.) F 9
POTATO (*Solanum tuberosum,* L.) B 2, C 12, F 4
POTATO, sweet (*Ipomoea batatas,* Lam.) C 2, C 13, F 2
PRIMROSE (*Primula vulgaris,* Huds.) F 5
PRIVET (*Ligustrum vulgare,* L.) B 2
PRIVET (*Ligustrum,* sp.) F 2, F 4, F 5, F 8
PRUNE, Italian (*Prunus domestica,* L.) D 3, D 7, F 18
PUMPKIN (*Cucurbita pepo,* L.) B 11, B 12, C 2
PURSLANE (*Portulaca oleracea,* L.) F 9
PYRACANTHA (*Pyracantha,* sp.) D 3

Q.

QUINCE (*Cydonia,* sp.) C 7, F 6

R.

RADISH (*Raphanus sativus,* L.) B 2, C 2, E 4, F 2, F 5, F 9
RAGWEED (*Ambrosia artemisiifolia,* L.) C 2
RAGWEED, giant (*Ambrosia trifida,* L.) F 4
RASPBERRY (*Rubus idaeus,* L.) D 3
RHODODENDRON (*Rhododendron,* sp.) D 3, F 4
RHODOTYPOS (*Rhodotypos,* sp.) F 5
RHUBARB (*Rheum Rhaponticum,* L.) C 2, F 4
RICE (*Oryza sativa,* L.) F 3
ROSE, tea (*Rosa odorata,* Sweet) D 3, F 5
ROSE (*Rosa,* sp.) C 10, F 2, F 4, F 7, F 9, F 12, F 24
ROSEBUD (*Rosa,* sp.) F 7
RYE (*Secale cereale,* L.) B 2, C 2, E 2, F 22

S.

SAFFLOWER (*Carthamus tinctorius,* L.) C 2
SALVIA (*Salvia,* sp.) F 8, F 9
SARCOCOCCA (*Sarcococca,* sp.) F 8
SASSAFRASS (*Sassafras albidum,* (Nutt.) Nees.) F 5
SAXIFRAGE (*Saxifrage,* sp.) F 8
SERVICEBERRY (*Amelanchier alnifolia,* Nutt.) D 3
SNOWBERRY (*Symphoricarpos albus,* Blake) B 2, B 17
SORGHUM (*Sorghum vulgare,* Pers.) C 2, C 15, D 3, E 4, F 2, F 4
SORREL (*Rumex,* sp.) F 4

SOYBEAN (*Glycine max,* Merr.) C 2, E 4, F 2, F 5, F 9, F 16, F 17
SPINACH (*Spinacea oleracea,* L.) B 2, B 10, B 12, C 2, E 4, F 2
SPRUCE, blue (*Picea pungens,* Englm.) D 3, F 4
SPRUCE, white (*Picea glauca* (Moench.) Voss.) D 3
SPRUCE (*Picea,* sp.) F 7
SQUASH (*Cucurbita maxima,* Duchesne) C 2, F 2
SQUASH (*Cucurbita moschata,* Duchesne) F 5
SQUASH, summer (*Curcurbita pepo,* L.) C 8, D 3
STRAWBERRY (*Fragaria,* sp.) D 3, F 8, F 9
SUMAC, smooth (*Rhus glabra,* L.) D 3
SUMAC, (*Rhus,* sp.) F 4
SUNFLOWER (*Helianthus annuus,* L.) E 2, F 5, F 6, F 9
SUNFLOWER (*Helianthus,* sp.) C 2, D 3, F 8
SWEETGUM (*Liquidambar styraciflua,* L.) F 4, F 5
SWEET PEA (*Lathyrus odoratus,* L.) C 2
SWISS CHARD (*Beta vulgaris* var. *cicla,* L.) C 2
SYCAMORE (*Platanus occidentalis,* L.) B 2, B 10

T.

TEA (*Thea,* sp) D 5
TOBACCO (*Nicotiana glauca,* Grah.) F 9
TOBACCO (*Nicotiana glutinosa,* L.) E 2
TOBACCO (*Nicotiana tabacum,* L.) B 2, B 14, E 4, F 2, F 5, F 6, F 9
TOBACCO (*Nicotiana,* sp.) E 7, E 8, E 13, E 14, F 4, F 8, F 13
TOMATO (*Lycopersicon esculentum,* Mill.) B 2, D 3, E 4, E 10, F 2, F 4-9
TOUCH-ME-NOT (*Impatiens,* sp.) E 4
TREEOFHEAVEN (*Ailanthus altissima,* Mill.) D 3, F 4, F 5
TULIP (*Tulipa Gesneriana,* L.) D 3
TULIP (*Tulipa,* sp.) F 5
TURNIP (*Brassica rapa,* L.) C 2

V.

VELVET-WEED (*Gaura parviflora,* Dougl.) C 2
VENUS-LOOKING-GLASS (*Specularia perfoliata,* (L.) A.DC) F 5
VERBENA (*Verbena canadensis,* Brit.) C 2
VIBURNUM (*Viburnum,* sp.) F 7, F 8
VINCA (*Vinca,* sp.) F 8
VIOLET (*Viola,* sp.) C 2, D 3
VIRGINIA CREEPER (*Parthenocissus quinquefolia,* Planch.) D 3, F 5

W.

WALNUT (*Juglans,* sp.) B 3
WALNUT, black (*Juglans nigra,* L.) D 3
WALNUT, English (*Juglans regia,* L.) D 3
WANDERING JEW (*Zebrina,* sp.) F 5
WEEPING WILLOW (*Salix babylonica,* L.) B 2
WHEAT (*Triticum aestivum,* L.) B 2
WHEAT (*Triticum sativum,* Lam.) E 4
WHEAT (*Triticum,* sp.) B 20, C 2, C 15, D 3
WILLOW (*Salix,* sp.) D 3, F 8
WISTERIA (*Wisteria,* sp.) F 4
WITCH HAZEL (*Hamamelis virginiana,* L.) F 5, F 18

Y.

YELLOW WOOD (*Cladrastis lutea,* Koch.) F 4
YEW (*Taxus,* sp.) B 1, F 4, F 5
YEW (*Taxus cuspidata,* Sieb. & Zucc.) D 3

Z.

ZINNIA (*Zinnia,* sp.) C 14, E 4, F 5
ZINNIA (*Zinnia elegans,* Lorenz) C 2